The American Writer in England

Henry James (no. 216)

THE AMERICAN
WRITER IN ENGLAND

An Exhibition
Arranged in Honor of the
Sesquicentennial of the University of Virginia

With a Foreword by
Gordon N. Ray

and

an Introduction by
C. Waller Barrett

The University Press of Virginia

Charlottesville

Grateful acknowledgment is made to quote the letter
of Henry Adams, by permission of the Massachusetts
Historical Society; letters from *Selected Letters of Robert
Frost*, edited by Lawrence Thompson, copyright ©
1964 by Holt, Rinehart and Winston, Inc., reprinted
by permission of the Estate of Robert Frost and Holt,
Rinehart and Winston, Inc.; "The Gift Outright,"
from *Complete Poems of Robert Frost*, copyright 1942 by
Robert Frost, reprinted by permission of Holt, Rinehart and Winston, Inc.; letters of Henry James, by permission of Leon Edel; and letters of Sinclair Lewis and
Thomas Wolfe, by permission of Melville Cane.

FOREWORD

IN HIS introduction Mr. Barrett has sufficiently emphasized the literary and human interest of this exhibit. I shall try to suggest briefly its bibliographical and historical importance, both in itself and as a sample of the great collection from which it is drawn.

In the past the subject of Anglo-American literary relations has been relatively neglected by both English and American scholars, but there are signs that it is finally beginning to receive the attention that it deserves. Well-informed editors of English texts now realize that, at least for books written during the last 150 years, they ignore American editions at their peril. In the first volume of the new Clarendon Dickens, for example, Mrs. Kathleen Tillotson has shown that the two editions of *Oliver Twist* printed by Lea and Blanchard of Philadelphia in 1839 are "unique texts" which "enable the editor to distinguish between variants which were [the English printers'] errors (undetected by Dickens) and those which are the author's deliberate changes."

Still more deserving of detailed study are the effects upon American thought and culture of the overwhelming availability of English books in this country before the passage of the international copyright law of 1891. Thirty years earlier Harper and Brothers had advertised a "NEW DESCRIPTIVE CATALOGUE . . . which will be found to comprise a large proportion of the standard and most esteemed works in English Literature—COMPREHENDING MORE THAN TWO THOUSAND VOLUMES—which are offered, in most cases, at less than one half the cost of similar productions in England." Less than half the price, be it remembered, of English *reprints*. At this period English novels were sold by Harper and Brothers, often "beautifully illustrated" and accompanied by appetizing "opinions of the British Press," for $.25 to $.75 in paper and $1.00 to $1.50 in cloth, figures substantially lower than those at which American novels were offered. Because of their superior interest and lower price English works continued to be far more widely read in this country than American, at least until the end of the century, and it is no wonder that the American critic W. C. Brownell wrote in the 1890s of "England's cultural dependency, ourselves."

Even though they also had some competitive advantage abroad in the absence of international copyright, American authors played no comparable role in English culture. Nonetheless, the English did read American books, Sydney Smith to the contrary; and as this exhibition amply demonstrates, Irving, Cooper, Poe, Hawthorne, Longfellow, Mark Twain, and others attained considerable popularity in England. Indeed, English readers were sometimes readier to appreciate certain kinds of merit in American books than were native readers. During the early years of his writing career Herman Melville was received quite as cordially in England as at home, and it may well be that his vogue faded less rapidly there. An interesting bit of evidence on this point has recently come my way in the manuscript diary for 1870 of Shirley Brooks, a prominent journalist and novelist who in that year became editor of *Punch*. Under the date of October 21 Brooks noted of a visit to Portslade near Brighton:

Pretty churchyard. Among monuments, one to a gentleman killed by a coach accident at Carlisle, 10 days after marriage, & to another, I think his brother, who sailed from Singapore, & of whom, or of his Ship, nothing was ever heard again. Reminded me of the capital description of a seaport church in my favourite book, "The Whale."

The reader will remember the marble tablets commemorating sailors lost at sea in the New Bedford Whaleman's Chapel of *Moby-Dick*.

This example from my own collection leads me to a salutary confession. When I visited Charlottesville last fall, I spent a couple of hours in the Barrett Library. My own collecting has centered on nineteenth-century English authors, but in a nonconsecutive way I have also taken an interest in first English editions of nineteenth-century American authors. With regard to two segments of this little subcollection I foolishly thought that I could compete with Mr. Barrett. A sad awakening was in store for me.

During a tour of the Lake Country many years ago I visited Ewen Ker's shop in Kendal just as he was unpacking a collection of novels from a country house library. Among them was a run of the first English editions of Charles Brockden Brown, chiefly in original boards, which I duly bought. These are editions of real interest (we know, for example, that this was the form in which Shelley read Brown), and they have a deserved reputation for rarity. I discovered that Mr. Barrett has them too and that his copies are on the whole in better condition than mine.

The first author whose books I collected with real seriousness was Henry James, who to my mind belongs quite as much to English as to American literature. Slowly and somewhat painfully I obtained all of the first English editions of his fiction. Their condition leaves little to be desired since over the years I have been able to replace good copies with better. (This was by no means an easy task, I may mention, since the early titles in particular, some of which were published in editions as small as 250 copies, have become notoriously difficult to find.) But once again I had to concede superiority to Mr. Barrett. Not only are his copies the equal of mine, but in many cases they bear presentation inscriptions in James's hand.

In this foreword I have taken for granted the importance of textual and bibliographical studies, as I am certainly entitled to do at the university which is the home of Mr. Fredson Bowers. No doubt the recent attack in the *New York Review of Books* on the Center for Editions of American Authors of the Modern Language Association of America raises complex questions of taste and emphasis. It must be obvious at the same time, however, that this attack derives in part from the alarm of amateurs at seeing rigorous professional standards applied to a subject in which they have a vested interest. Here, at least, the issue is not in doubt. As the American learned world has come to full maturity since the Second World War, a similar animus has shown itself and been discredited in field after field from botany to folklore. In the long run professional standards always prevail.

It is exactly when such standards are applied that the importance of a collection such as Mr. Barrett has assembled is truly seen. The vast mine of books, periodicals, ephemera of all sorts, and above all letters and manuscripts, of which this exhibit offers a representative cross section, is a *sine qua non* for the orderly, professional study of America's literary past. Since the time has long since gone by when a similar collection could be assembled, the University of Virginia is assured of a basic resource in this area which few other universities can match, and it is through the accumulation of such basic resources that universities achieve and maintain greatness.

Gordon N. Ray
President, John Simon
Guggenheim Foundation

PREFACE

THE exhibition this catalogue accompanies is not designed to trace the influence of English literature on American writers. Nor is it intended to portray the history of the development of a native American literature. The purpose is rather to show the extent to which early American writing was an outgrowth of the English literature of the period, the way the American writer developed when directly exposed to British life and culture, and the evolution in the end of an independent American literature which nevertheless did not lose the inspiration and fertilizing influence of its British parent.

The various items in the exhibition are intended to demonstrate this process. There are, of course, many hundreds of books and manuscripts that fit this category, and it has been necessary to make a selection. The exhibits are therefore representative rather than inclusive. Emphasis has naturally been placed on the major American writers who spent various periods of time in England. Also included are other native writers of recognized merit whose works illuminate the theme. Most of the authors exhibited were directly exposed to English influence through short or long residence in the "fair isle." Even Poe spent five years of his childhood in Great Britain and began his education there. One outstanding exception among others is Walt Whitman, who never visited Britain. He is included because of the tremendous impact, favorable and unfavorable, that *Leaves of Grass* made on the British people and because of Whitman's constant awareness of our English origins. Whitman was fully alive to his literary contemporaries in Britain. Thoreau, too, is included for similar reasons.

Many books have been consulted in the preparation of this

catalogue and its introduction. An extended bibliography would be out of place here, but I would like to acknowledge a considerable debt to six works:

Jacob Blanck. *Bibliography of American Literature*. New Haven, 1955–63.

I. R. Brussel. *Anglo-American First Editions*. Part Two: *West to East*. London, 1936.

Kay S. House. *Reality and Myth in American Literature*. New York, 1966.

The author of this valuable work paralleled many of my researches, particularly in the use of quotations.

Merle Johnson and Jacob Blanck. *American First Editions*. New York, 1942.

Stanley J. Kunitz and Howard Haycraft. *American Authors, 1600–1900*. New York, 1938.

Arthur Hobson Quinn. *American Fiction: An Historical and Critical Survey*. New York, 1936.

Grateful acknowledgment is made to the Committee for the Sesquicentennial Celebration of the University of Virginia for the financial aid that made this publication possible. I am deeply indebted to the University Press of Virginia for enthusiastic support and invaluable assistance; to Mr. Ray W. Frantz, Jr., University Librarian, for his constant encouragement and advice; to Mr. William H. Runge, Curator of Rare Books at the Alderman Library, and to members of his staff, Mrs. Nancy Boles and Mrs. Virginia Kerr, for their dedicated efforts in arranging the exhibition and preparing the catalogue; and finally to Miss Anne Freudenberg, Curator of Manuscripts, and her associates, Mr. Edmund Berkeley and Mrs. Elizabeth Ryall Schubert, for their unfailing assistance in making promptly available the manuscripts consulted.

C. Waller Barrett

CONTENTS

INTRODUCTION
THE AMERICAN WRITER IN ENGLAND

IN EXPLORING the subject of the American writer in England, one might well take a look at the impact of the American colonies on the English people. The early colonists were, of course, dependent on the mother country; they brought with them the language, the literature, the customs of Britain. A century and a half were to pass before the Americans began their struggle for independence and, simultaneously, began to develop a purely American idiom and to lay the foundations for a native literature.

All of this is well known, but what we tend to forget is the thrust of the American dream on the British people. This new land, offering individual religious and political freedom and presumably flowing with milk and honey, appealed to their imagination as a new Eden offering the opportunity of a new Golden Age, a Utopia. In 1606, before Jamestown, Michael Drayton composed an ode that contains the earliest challenge to American writers:

> Britons, you stay too long.
> Quickly aboard bestow you;
>   And with a merry gale
>   Swell your stretch'd sail
> With vows as strong
> As the winds that blow you.
>   .   .   .   .   .
> And cheerfully at sea,
> Success you still entice,
>   To get the pearl and gold;
>   And ours to hold;
> Virginia,
> Earth's only paradise.
>   .   .   .   .   .

> And as there plenty grows
> 　　Of laurel everywhere,—
> Apollo's sacred tree,
> 　　You, it may see,
> A poet's brows
> To crown, that may sing there.

Shakespeare might well have been thinking of America when the sailors in *The Tempest*, approaching a "brave new world," found themselves in "the still vexed Bermoothes."

Bishop Berkeley a century later wrote his *Verses on the Prospect of Planting Arts and Learning in America:*

> The Muse, disgusted at an age and clime
> 　　Barren of every glorious theme,
> In distant lands now waits a better time,
> 　　Producing subjects worthy fame.
>
> 　　·　　·　　·　　·　　·
>
> In happy climes, the seat of innocence,
> 　　Where nature guides and virtue rules;
> Where men shall not impose for truth and sense
> 　　The pedantry of courts and schools.
>
> There shall be sung another golden age.
> 　　The rise of empires and of arts,
> The good and great, inspiring epic rage,
> 　　The wisest heads and noblest hearts.
>
> Not such as Europe breeds in her decay,
> 　　Such as she bred when fresh and young,
> When heavenly flame did animate her clay,
> 　　By future poets shall be sung.
>
> Westward the course of empire takes its way;
> 　　The first four acts already past,
> A fifth shall close the drama with the day—
> 　　Time's noblest offspring is the last.

In 1852 Philarète Chasles, professor in the Collège de France, described the background for the emergence of a native literature:

The United States . . . wants that dawn and penumbra which gives perspective. The very tongue is not native to the soil; it has crossed the sea, and naturalized itself on that side of the ocean. To preserve the purity of their style, American writers are forced to keep their regard constantly fixed upon the mother country where are found their types and models. If they innovate, they fear vulgarity or emphasis. In this respect they are like those modern writers, who use a dead language, and fancy that they can thus restore to us Cicero, Demosthenes, Livy; forgetting that it is the social life of a people which gives energy and life to a language, and that an idiom detached from national society and manners, is a branch detached from the tree, and deprived of its sap. . . .

The republicans of the United States, a virgin people, full of grandeur, whose struggle with nature is not yet ended; all of whose energy must necessarily be directed to the foundation of cities and the development of industry; a nation whose Future is their country; who have no Past—hardly born and already a giant—which had no infancy, no childhood, and whose maturity precedes its youth—not recognizing in their history any of those transitions from feebleness to virility; any of those epochs, and chain of which, ornamented by tradition, receives later, the consecration of poetry.

Here are soldiers, legislators, artisans, a strong noble race sufficient for today. Poets will be born hereafter.

Many decades passed before the American writer began to cast off the intellectual shackles of the mother country and to use native material in the attempt to develop a native American literature. An examination of the early writings shows how much they owed to the British.

Perhaps the first attempt at American fiction was *A Pretty Story Written in . . . 2774* by Francis Hopkinson, a signer of the Declaration of Independence. This slight story is an allegorical satire in which King George is portrayed as an old nobleman who tyrannizes over his colonial children of the "new farm." He in turn is ruled by his wife and steward, who represent Parliament and Lord North.

It is generally agreed that the first American novel was *The Power of Sympathy* (1789) by William Hill Brown. The work is clearly an imitation of the English novel of the period. It is in epistolary form and includes two episodes of seduction in the manner of Samuel Richardson.

A much better novel and the first American best seller was *Charlotte* (1791), later *Charlotte Temple,* by Susan Rowson.

This work, also in epistolary form, concerns an English schoolgirl who elopes to America with a British officer and is seduced and abandoned to die in childbirth. The child survives to become the heroine of a sequel, *Charlotte's Daughter* (1828).

Another novel of this early period was *The Emigrants*, probably written in 1787 but not published until 1793, in London. The author was Gilbert Imlay, a native of New Jersey who, after travels in Kentucky and elsewhere in America, went to London to live. He became the lover of Mary Wollstonecraft and the father of her daughter Fanny. "He saw [Mary] for the last time in 1796, just before her marriage to [William] Godwin, the birth of Mary Godwin (Shelley's second wife), and her death."

Other works of fiction written in the style of the British novel were the anonymous and very popular *History of Constantius & Pulchera* (1794); *The History of Maria Kittle* (1797), by Ann Eliza Bleecker; the anonymous *Amelia; or, The Faithless Briton* (1798); and *Fortune's Foot-Ball* (1797–98), by James Butler, an Englishman who emigrated to Harrisburg, Pennsylvania.

After the turn of the century Americans began to assert their independence of British literary forms and traditions even when their methods and plots still betrayed the influence of the old country. Among the more independent was Charles Brockden Brown, called our first professional novelist; he produced six novels in three years. Although he made use of the Gothic atmosphere which characterized many British novels at this time, he laid his scenes in America and used native characters. His novels were reprinted in London and went through several editions.

James K. Paulding, friend and collaborator of Washington Irving, published *The Diverting History of John Bull and Brother*

Jonathan in 1812. Paulding expressed decided opinions on Great Britain and on travelers such as Mrs. Trollope and Fanny Wright. He believed "that Squire Bull and Brother Jonathan were too much alike to be right down good friends." The contrast between England and America was featured in *A Sketch of Old England* (1822) and in *John Bull in America* (1825).

Another noted writer of fiction was William A. Caruthers of Virginia. He published *The Cavaliers of Virginia* in 1834–35. The scene of Caruthers' novel is laid in Jamestown shortly after the restoration of Charles II. This work was followed by *The Knights of the Horse-Shoe* (1845), an account of the westward explorations of Governor Alexander Spotswood of Virginia in the early eighteenth century.

In 1825 Lydia Maria Child, ardent feminist and abolitionist, published a novel concerned with the Stamp Tax agitation, *The Rebels, or Boston before the Revolution.*

John Neal, born in Falmouth, now a part of Portland, Maine, went to England in 1823 and became the first American to contribute regularly to English periodicals. In *Brother Jonathan* (1825) he portrayed American characters for British readers. "The cupidity of the Yankees, the vulgarity of manners and customs in New York City are emphasized."

Royall Tyler, dramatist, poet, and novelist, was the author of the first comedy written by a citizen of the United States and professionally produced in America (1787). His play *The Contrast* (1790) was preceded only by the oriental drama *The Prince of Parthia* (1765), written by a colonial, Thomas Godfrey, and produced at the Southwark Theater, Philadelphia, in 1767. *The Contrast* was a pronounced success and was repeated five times in New York as well as being played in Baltimore, Philadelphia, Boston, Charleston, and Richmond.

Other native dramatists were Hugh Henry Brackenridge

of Pennsylvania and William Dunlap of New Jersey. Bracken-ridge was coauthor, with Thomas Jefferson's journalistic friend Philip Freneau, of the stirring poem *The Rising Glory of America* (1772). He also composed two verse plays, *The Battle of Bunkers-Hill* (1776), an ardent appeal to American patriot-ism, and *The Death of General Montgomery* (1777), a dramatic presentation of a dark period in the Revolution for American arms. The latter play invokes "the ghost of General Wolfe who reproaches the King and Parliament in good round fash-ion." William Dunlap was a remarkable figure who acted as theater manager, playwright, novelist, artist, and historian. When he was sixteen, his father sent him to England to study with Benjamin West. He became completely enamored of the stage. His play *The Father* (1789) was the second play by an American citizen to be professionally produced and the first one to be printed. Perhaps Dunlap's greatest effort was his tragedy of the Revolution, *Andre*, first performed and pub-lished in 1798, one of the earliest plays to have George Wash-ington as a character.

John Howard Payne of New York City sailed for England in 1813 and remained there nineteen years. A prolific play-wright, he produced about sixty plays. Notable among these was *Clari*, which appeared at Covent Garden in 1823. This play contains the famous lyric *Home! Sweet Home!* Payne collaborated with Washington Irving on *Charles the Second; or, The Merry Monarch*, produced in London in 1824.

The foregoing achievements in fiction, poetry, and drama make it apparent that American writers of the period were beginning to experience a burst of creative energy that would lay firm foundations for a national literature. The time was ripe for the advent of Irving, Cooper, Simms, Hawthorne, and Melville in the field of fiction; for the flowering of the New England poets and philosophers, Emerson, Longfellow,

Lowell, and Thoreau; and, importantly, for the emergence of Walt Whitman in Brooklyn. The use of American themes and background is discussed by William Gilmore Simms in his preface to *The Yemassee:*

"The Yemassee" is proposed as an *American* romance. It is so styled as much of the material could have been furnished by no other country. Something too much of extravagance—so some may think,—even beyond the usual license of fiction—may enter into certain parts of the narrative. On this subject, it is enough for me to say, that the popular faith yields abundant authority for the wildest of its incidents. The natural romance of my country has been my object, and I have not dared beyond it.

The keystone of the native literary edifice was the so-called "Knickerbocker's" *History of New York*, published by Washington Irving in 1809, the year that Jefferson left the presidency. This irreverent and imaginary history owed little or nothing to the prevailing modes of English writing. It was a different story, however, with Irving's next work, *The Sketch Book*, which was written entirely in England and was an amalgam of essays on English literature and customs joined to two immortal tales with American backgrounds, *Rip Van Winkle* and *The Legend of Sleepy Hollow*. At the time *The Sketch Book* was being published, the critic Sydney Smith of Edinburgh uttered the famous remark, "In the four quarters of the globe, who reads an American book?" He was answered very quickly as a host of English readers succumbed delightedly to the charms of *The Sketch Book*. All told, Irving spent a dozen years in England, and one of his noteworthy accomplishments was the interpretation of the British, literary and otherwise, to American readers.

William Cullen Bryant was a voice heard in both England and America. This precocious poet composed *The Embargo* at thirteen. As a political satire aimed at Jefferson's foreign policy it pleased the British. At seventeen Bryant wrote the durable *Thanatopsis*. Richard Henry Dana the elder refused the two poems for the *North American Review*, because, he said, no one in America could write in such a style and the poems were a hoax. Once he became convinced they were genuine, he published them with alacrity. Washington Irving arranged for the publication of Bryant's poems in England in 1832. In order to avoid offending British sensibilities, it was necessary to change a line in the poem *Marion's Men*. The offending line and the next were:

> The British soldier trembles
> When Marion's name is told.

This was changed to read:

> The foeman trembles in his camp
> When Marion's name is told.

Irving wrote a dedication for the English edition in which he said:

The descriptive writings of Mr. Bryant are essentially American. They transport us into the depths of the solemn primeval forest—to the shores of the lonely lake—the banks of the wild nameless stream, or the brow of the rocky upland rising like a promontory from amidst a wide ocean of foliage. . . . His writings are imbued with the independent spirit, and the buoyant aspirations incident to a youthful, a free, and a rising country.

Another American poet, from Virginia, made an early contribution to world literature. Edgar Allan Poe was born in Boston in 1809, the year of publication of "Knickerbocker's" *History*. He had five years of schooling in England and Scotland, but he spent a considerable part of his short and tragic life in Richmond. Unappreciated and condemned in his native land, he became celebrated abroad, especially in France. The world has rendered its verdict on him: a supreme artist. In the words of Algernon Charles Swinburne, "Only once has there sounded out of [America] one pure note of original song worth singing and echoed from the singing of no other man; a note . . . utterly true, rich, clear, and native to the singer; the short exquisite music, subtle and simple and sombre and sweet, of Edgar Poe."

The American novel came into its own with the publication of *The Spy* in 1821 by James Fenimore Cooper. This fictional treatment of certain incidents in Washington's campaign in Westchester, New York, has been called "the first living American novel." It was published within a year in London. The novels of the Leatherstocking series were all published promptly in England and were avidly read by the British. D. H. Lawrence declares that the colonists came to America for two reasons:

> To slough the old European consciousness completely.
> To grow a new skin underneath, a new form.

And he continues:

The Leatherstocking novels create . . . the true myth of America. She starts old, old, wrinkled and writhing in the old skin. And there is a gradual sloughing of the old skin, towards a new youth. It is the myth of America.

The question of British influence on Cooper's novels of the sea is a moot one. His first, *The Pilot*, followed Walter Scott's *Pirate*. Did Scott influence Cooper, or, as many believe, did Cooper influence Scott? In any event the scenes of Scott's novel are mostly laid on shore whereas Cooper gives a description of human beings struggling and conquering the sea.

Cooper first sailed for Europe in 1826. As his ship moved away from land, the last words he heard were, "You'll never come back." In 1833 when he returned to New York harbor, he shouted from the deck in a gesture of determined patriotism, "I have come back." While he was in England, Cooper arranged for the publication of *Notions of the Americans*, described as "a deliberate, almost belligerent assault on British prejudices toward the United States." His attitude is revealed by what he said on being told that his book pleased the British. His reply was, "It wasn't what I intended then." Twenty-six of Cooper's books, including *Notions of the Americans*, were published first in England, principally because of the state of the copyright laws. Cooper wrote:

The literature of the United States has, indeed, two powerful obstacles to conquer before (to use a mercantile expression) it can ever enter the markets of its own country on terms of perfect equality with that of England. . . . The fact, that an American publisher can get an English work without money, must . . . have a tendency to repress a national literature. No man will pay a writer for an epic, a tragedy, a sonnet, a history, or a romance, when he can get a work of equal merit for nothing.

Emerson paid his respects to this situation when he wrote:

See what books fill our libraries. Every book we read, every biography, play, romance, in whatever form is still English history and manners. So that a sensible Englishman once said to me, "As long as you do not grant us copyright, we shall have the teaching of you."

William Gilmore Simms has been called, somewhat deprecatingly, the "Southern Cooper." The body of his writings, however, dispels the idea that he was a mere follower of the New York novelist. Indeed, Simms had a somewhat wider range than Cooper, since in addition to fiction he produced creditable poetry and history, as well as several plays which were never produced. He is best known for his novels of the colonial period, of which the most noted is *The Yemassee* (1835), and for his Revolutionary War series. Although Simms never visited England, the English are indebted to him for *A Supplement to the Plays of William Shakspeare* (1848), which was the first American printing of seven plays formerly attributed to Shakespeare.

Nathaniel Parker Willis was born in Portland, Maine, in 1806, one year before Longfellow. Like Longfellow, he became the darling of London society; he was described by an English lady as "more like the best of our peers' sons than a rough republican." His play *Tortesa the Usurer* (1839) was described by Poe as "by far the best play from the pen of an American author." Many of Willis's books were first published in London. In *Paul Fane* (1857) he "struck that note of the resentment of the artist against those who accept him merely as a celebrity and not as a human being . . . in his picture of the poet who is sought after as a lion and as a lover by various women in England, but is treated by only one as a possible husband."

Emerson visited England in 1833 for a few months and again in 1847. On his second trip he renewed his famous friendship with Thomas Carlyle and gathered the material that was published in *English Traits*, issued in both England and America in 1856. Here, again, is a key book—an interpretation of the British to the American people. Emerson described with friendly acuity English characteristics of race, manners, ability, aristocracy, universities, religion, and literature.

In 1837 Emerson issued his clarion call to the American scholar:

This confidence in the unsearched might of man belongs, by all motives, by all prophecy, by all preparation, to the American Scholar. We have listened too long to the courtly muses of Europe. The spirit of the American freeman is already suspected to be timid, imitative, tame. . . . Not so, brothers and friends—please God, ours shall not be so. We will walk on our own feet; we will work with our own hands; we will speak our own minds. The study of letters will no longer be a name for pity, for doubt, and for sensual indulgence. The dread of man and the love of man shall be a wall of defence and a wreath of joy around all. A nation of men will for the first time exist, because each believes himself inspired by the Divine Soul which also inspires all men.

Emerson's great friend and neighbor in Concord, the acrid philosopher Henry David Thoreau, never left the United States. One wonders what the British would have thought of the physical presence of this homespun advocate of the uses of nature. In any event they received *Walden* with open arms, and one of the best biographies of Thoreau was written by an Englishman, Henry S. Salt. Thoreau for his part planted a time bomb in the heart of the British Empire with his essay,

Civil Disobedience, which provided the effective slogan for Mahatma Gandhi's campaign for Indian independence.

In 1853 Nathaniel Hawthorne was appointed United States consul at Liverpool. His fame as the author of *The Scarlet Letter* assured him a warm welcome in England. Hawthorne's English notebooks cover his experiences of four years in the old country. From these he published, simultaneously in London and Boston in 1863, *Our Old Home: A Series of English Sketches*. Hawthorne reveals his sentiments about England in the conclusion of the chapter "Consular Experiences": "I hope I do not compromise my American patriotism by acknowledging that I was often conscious of a fervent hereditary attachment to the native soil of our forefathers, and felt it to be our own Old Home."

Hawthorne was instrumental in rescuing an American woman writer, Delia Bacon, who had come to London to expound her idea that Shakespeare was not the author of the plays. She was the first "Baconian," and for a time many scholars were attracted to her theory that Shakespeare's plays were written by a triumvirate consisting of Bacon, Raleigh, and Spenser. She had been sent to London by one of her converts, none other than Ralph Waldo Emerson. She lived there in destitute circumstances until she was discovered by Hawthorne, who wrote an introduction for her work *The Philosophy of the Plays of Shakspere Unfolded* and arranged for its publication in 1857.

Harriet Beecher Stowe, born the same year as Delia Bacon, visited England in 1853, 1856, and 1859. The author of *Uncle Tom's Cabin*, first published in book form in 1852, was received with acclaim by English abolitionists. The celebrated artist George Cruikshank illustrated the English edition of *Uncle Tom*, published in 1852. Her British readers were alienated years later, however, when she attempted to vindicate Lady Byron by raking the embers of the almost forgotten scandal. She wrote two books publicizing the incestuous relations between Byron and his half-sister, Augusta Leigh.

Two years after Henry Wadsworth Longfellow died, his bust was placed in the Poet's Corner in Westminster Abbey, the only American poet ever to be so honored. Longfellow attracted a tremendous following in England. *The Song of Hiawatha* and *The Courtship of Miles Standish* were first printed there. He didn't appeal to the critics so much as to the middle and lower classes, to the nobility, and to royalty. Queen Victoria was one of his ardent admirers.

James Russell Lowell was a bit embarrassed when he made his appearance in London in 1880 as the new American minister. He remembered his early work *The Biglow Papers*, in which he had rather bitterly satirized Southern slaveholders and their British sympathizers. By this time, however, his natural conservatism had taken over, and his genuine devotion to English literature overcame any lingering prejudice. The literary world in Britain remembered his elegant essays on British poets. They considered, too, that his own poetry owed a good deal to Tennyson and Byron. In the words of one commentator, "He was popular and successful; he was the orator when Coleridge's bust was unveiled at Westminster Abbey, and in 1884, he was made rector of the University of St. Andrew's in Edinburgh—an honorary absentee office."

Lowell spoke on literature at the 100th anniversary of Washington's inauguration in 1889, and he adverted to our English background:

Scarcely had we become a nation when the only part of the Old World whose language we understood began to ask in various tones of despondency where was our literature. We would not improvise Virgils or Miltons, though we made an obliging effort to do it. With a language in compass and variety inferior to none that has ever been the instrument of human thought or passion or sentiment, we had inherited the forms and precedents of a literature altogether worthy of it. But these forms and precedents we were to adapt to novel conditions, themselves still in solution, tentative, formless, atom groping after atom, rather through blind instinct than with conscious purpose. Why wonder if our task proved as long as it was difficult?

Herman Melville's brother Gansevoort sold the publication rights to Herman's first book, *Typee*, to John Murray in London late in 1845. The work was published there, under the title *Narrative of a Four Months' Residence among the Natives of a Valley of the Marquesas Islands*, shortly before it appeared in America. There followed in the same year a revised New York edition with an added story, or rather a short sequel, entitled *The Story of Toby*. The revised American text eliminated a sentence that had offended the tender sensibilities of American readers. Melville had described the boarding of the ship *Dolly* by a flock of damsels from the island of Nukuheva:

> All [of the nymphs] succeeded in getting up the ship's side, where they hung dripping with the brine and glowing from the bath, their jet-black tresses streaming over their shoulders, and half-enveloping their otherwise naked forms. . . .
>
> Their appearance perfectly amazed me; their extreme youth, the light clear brown of their complexions, their delicate features, and inexpressibly graceful figures, their softly molded limbs, and free unstudied action, seemed as strange as it was beautiful. . . .
>
> Our ship was now wholly given up to every species of riot and debauchery. Not the feeblest barrier was interposed between the unholy passions of the crew and their unlimited gratification.

The final sentence was the offending one and it was dropped, thus protecting the American public from the final touch in Melville's graphic description of the crew venting its lust on innocent, if somewhat complaisant, native damsels.

Melville's works continued to be published in London with the issuance of *Omoo* (1847), *Mardi* (1849), and *White-Jacket* (1850). Then in 1851 there appeared in London a remarkable novel in three volumes called *The Whale*. Thus the mighty epic that we know as *Moby-Dick* saw the light of day. It has been described as America's contribution to the world novel, but it did not help Melville's popularity with the general public. In the very year that *Moby-Dick* was issued, Melville's publishers refused him a further advance because he had already had $700 and they thought his future earnings were likely to decrease. An English edition of *Redburn* did, however, appear in 1853. During the last half of his life Melville lived in comparative obscurity, and when he died in 1891, the event was barely noticed in the press.

Walt Whitman stirred the literary waters of England in 1855 with what has been called the great American poem, *Leaves of Grass*. Whitman never visited England; actually, he never left his native land. Nevertheless he had a host of English admirers, and when he was later described as poor and friendless, a flood of sympathetic articles and book orders came from the British Isles. William Michael Rossetti issued an edition of Whitman's poems (selected and expurgated) in London in 1868. A redoubtable English lady of literary leanings, Anne Gilchrist, read these poems and immediately fell in love with the poet. After two years of waiting and pining she wrote Whitman an extraordinary love letter offering herself to him body and soul. She yearned to become the poet's mate spiritually and physically and, she hoped, the mother of a noble progeny. She already had four children. Deeply embarrassed, Whitman attempted to dampen her ardor. Despite the virility of his poems, Whitman was not possessed of a strong heterosexual nature. As Mrs. Gilchrist advanced with unashamed passion, he retreated precipitately. In 1876, strongly against his wishes, she arrived in Philadelphia with three of her children and took a house there. Her hope that her physical presence might gain her ends was disappointed. She found the poet quite unable to live up to her erotic fancy and returned to England in 1879. On her death, six years later, her last words were of Whitman.

A dyed-in-the-wool Virginian, John Esten Cooke, produced a very successful novel of the colonial Virginia theater in *The Virginia Comedians*, presenting therein a picture of the carefree and irresponsible life of the time. After a notable achievement in his novels of the Civil War, Cooke made use of English material and scenes in such works as *Fairfax* (1868), which concerns Lord Fairfax and the young George Washington, *Out of the Foam* (1871), and *Her Majesty the Queen* (1873).

In 1871 a flamboyant figure appeared in London, sporting a full beard and dressed in frontier fashion with boots and a mammoth sombrero. This character, Cincinnatus Heine Miller, self-styled "Joaquin" Miller, quickly made friends with William Rossetti and other leading literary figures and in less than three years published four books in London. His *Songs of the Sierras* (1871) brought him a goodly measure of praise. An expert self-promoter, Miller was soon sporting a diamond ring which he said had been given to him by a duchess. He will be best remembered perhaps for his poem *Columbus* with its lines:

> He gained a world; he gave that world
> Its grandest lesson: "On! sail on!"

Joaquin Miller was not the only American to go abroad in 1871; in that year the first of three Californians, Ambrose Bierce, sailed for England. We call them "three Californians" because all began their serious literary work and made their early reputations in that state—but they were not born there. Ambrose Bierce was born in Ohio, Samuel L. Clemens (Mark Twain) in Missouri, and Bret Harte in New York. Bierce remained in England five years, published his first three books there, and contributed extensively to British humorous magazines. He followed in the footsteps of Charles Farrar Browne (Artemus Ward), who in 1866 had become a lion in London as the first representative of the American school of earthy, robust humor. Bierce's health dictated his return in 1876 to California, where he gained fame as the author of some of the finest short stories in the English language, collected in the volume *Tales of Soldiers and Civilians* (1891).

In 1878 Bret Harte departed for Germany to take up his appointment as United States consul in Crefeld, Germany. Shortly thereafter he became consul at Glasgow, Scotland. He had no presentiment that he would never return to his native land. Harte had become the most sought-after writer in America following the publication of *The Luck of Roaring Camp* and *Plain Language from Truthful James* (*The Heathen Chinee*). He had received from the *Atlantic Monthly* the most remunerative literary contract ever known in the United States up to that time. From this eminence his path had been rapidly downward, and he had been forced to seek a government appointment to try to make ends meet. His lack of money forced him to leave his wife and children at home. Harte landed in Plymouth, and he wrote his wife that he had only one strong feeling in "great, solid, earthy, powerful, and practical London. I am awfully lonely."

That Bret Harte did not lack for friends and admirers in England is shown by the fact that he was invited by the British Royal Academy to reply to the "Toast to Literature" at the 1879 dinner. His feelings of shyness and inferiority caused him to decline. The invitation was repeated the following year, and Harte found himself before the Prince of Wales and other members of the royal family, Prime Minister William E. Gladstone, Thomas Huxley, Anthony Trollope, and Robert Browning. The president proposed the toast:

I have now to ask you to drink to the interest of Science and Literature. . . . I shall call upon a writer who owes us no allegiance save that of friendship to a country in which he is now a guest. An English writer, nevertheless, for English is the tongue in which he delights the unnumerable host of his readers. This company will be glad, I am confident, of the opportunity thus offered to it of welcoming in its midst the great American humorist, Bret Harte.

Harte replied to the toast by a humorous reference to

the literary piracy going on on both sides of the Atlantic. He said:

I presume I am selected to answer this toast as the native of a country which reads more English books and pays less for them than any other nation. It has been settled by your reviewers that American Literature is American humor. . . . I consider that no higher compliment has been paid American humor than that the type of American drawn by your greatest English humorists has been supplanted by types drawn by Lowell, Artemus Ward and Mark Twain.

Samuel L. Clemens visited England regularly. In 1872 he wrote that he would rather live in England than America. Certainly, if public adulation had anything to do with it, he would have found himself thoroughly at home there. The high point of his British experience was receiving the honorary degree of Doctor of Letters from Oxford University. Thereafter he wore the scarlet gown on numerous occasions, including his daughter Clara's wedding. Many of Mark Twain's books were issued first in England, among them his best, *Tom Sawyer* (1876), *Life on the Mississippi* (1883), and *Huckleberry Finn* (1884). Unhappily, two of his works with English backgrounds, *The Prince and the Pauper* (1882) and *A Connecticut Yankee* (1889), were among his less successful productions. In any event there is considerable agreement among British critics with Ernest Hemingway's pronouncement that all modern American literature comes from one book, *Huckleberry Finn*.

F. Marion Crawford, a cosmopolitan author who was in and out of London frequently, was the son of the American sculptor Thomas Crawford, domiciled in Rome. His aunt was Julia Ward Howe, composer of *The Battle Hymn of the Republic*. Crawford's haphazard education included a year at Cambridge. As a result of his exposure to Italy he became a writer of Italian romances, of which he produced a long series. One of his best works, however, is generally considered to be *Via Crucis* (1899), in which he creates the character of Gilbert

Warde, a young English noble of Norman descent who becomes an exile as a result of the war between King Stephen and Queen Maud. Three of Crawford's other novels have largely English characters, *A Tale of a Lonely Parish* (1886), *Adam Johnstone's Son* (1895), and *The Undesirable Governess* (1910).

Harold Frederic, an early exponent of the realistic novel, sailed for England in 1884 to act as the London correspondent of the New York *Times*. His life in England was anything but serene as he found himself engaged in an attempt to maintain two households, one with his wife and another with his mistress, both with several children. He died of a paralytic stroke at forty-two. Although all of Frederic's novels were written in England, the scenes of the first eleven, including the finest, *The Damnation of Theron Ware* (1896), were laid in the United States. His last three novels, however, were concerned with English life: *March Hares* (1896), *Gloria Mundi* (1898), and *The Market-Place* (1899), the last a posthumous publication.

Henry James, like Bret Harte, made his home in England. He became a British subject as a protest against America's failure to join the Allies in the early years of the First World War. Ezra Pound, himself an expatriate, wrote about James's change in nationality:

The "Americans" will understand nothing whatsoever about it. They do not even know what they lost. They have not stopped for eight minutes to consider the meaning of his last public act. After a year of ceaseless labour, of letter writing, of argument, of striving in every way to bring in America on the side of civilization, he died of apoplexy.

During his long writing career James became the foremost interpreter of America to England and vice versa. In such books as *A Passionate Pilgrim*, *The Europeans*, *The Portrait of a Lady*, and *The Golden Bowl* he labored mightily in this effort. Pound wrote:

And the great labour, this labour of translation, of making America intelligible, or making it possible for individuals to meet across national borders. I think half the American idiom is recorded in Henry James' writing, and whole decades of American life that otherwise would have been utterly lost, wasted, rotting in the unhermetic jars of bad writing, of inaccurate writing.

A lifelong friend of Henry James, William Dean Howells, though born in poverty in Ohio, became the dean of American letters in his time. In addition to much editorial and critical work throughout his career, he found time to write some forty novels as well as juveniles, poems, plays, and miscellaneous essays. Of his novels, *The Rise of Silas Lapham* (1885) and *Indian Summer* (1886) are considered his finest efforts. Howells made numerous trips to England, his first occurring in 1882, and his letters and travel books reflect with charm "the mixture of pleasure and annoyance that he felt whenever he found himself again on the island from which all of his ancestors had migrated hardly more than a hundred years earlier." James Russell Lowell, United States minister to the Court of St. James from 1880 to 1885, opened many doors to his younger friend. At various times Howells enjoyed the society of many other American writers resident in London or visiting England, including Henry James, Bret Harte, Thomas Bailey Aldrich, Charles Dudley Warner, and John Hay.

Howells considered himself an exponent of realistic fiction as opposed to "'the old romantic ideals' of Scott, Balzac, Victor Hugo, Dickens, Thackeray and even Hawthorne." He was a great admirer of "divine Jane Austen," George Eliot, Goldsmith, and Trollope. Many of Howells's works were issued in English editions.

Stephen Crane, born in Newark, New Jersey, was another American who found the English atmosphere congenial. *The Red Badge of Courage* took England by storm. Crane passed his last few years in a vast, gloomy, run-down manor house called Brede Place, and there he welcomed his many friends and fervent admirers, including Henry James, H. G. Wells, and Joseph Conrad. He had married or perhaps not married a lady six years older than he who had been the proprietress of the "Hotel de Dream," a high-class house of manly recreation in Jacksonville, Florida. She was a woman of education, grace, and charm, and she moved with assurance among Crane's literary friends. Cora Crane—so-called—was an understanding and amiable companion for Stephen. Her only fault was, perhaps, a propensity for high living which kept him chained to his writing table grinding out stories and articles to meet the rapidly mounting debts. Ill and exhausted, he died in 1900 before his twenty-ninth birthday in the Black Forest of Germany. A few years after his death Cora returned to her former profession.

With the new century there came a realization that an independent American literature had been firmly established. A retrospective glance brought to view such authentic classics as *The Sketch Book*, *The Last of the Mohicans*, *The Scarlet Letter*, Poe's *Poems*, *Walden*, Emerson's *Essays*, *Moby-Dick*, *Leaves of Grass*, *Huckleberry Finn*, *The Luck of Roaring Camp*, *The Portrait of a Lady*, and *The Red Badge of Courage*. No longer was American writing to be considered a mere appendage to English letters. It had won its right to an independent existence.

Naturally, during the twentieth century American writers have continued to visit England and to derive inspiration therefrom. Thomas Wolfe, Ernest Hemingway, Scott Fitzgerald, Eugene O'Neill, Willa Cather, Mary Johnston, Booth Tarkington, and William Faulkner have made pilgrimages, and Anne Douglas Sedgwick went over and ultimately stayed. Nevertheless, their writings reflect the independent American spirit; they are in the American idiom.

In 1911 the man who was to become America's foremost

playwright, Eugene O'Neill, shipped out from Buenos Aires on the British tramp *Ikalis*, with a crew largely from Liverpool. O'Neill's experiences as an ordinary seaman were transmuted into the dramatic essence of a cycle of four plays in which the *Ikalis* is renamed the S/S *Glencairn*. The scene of three of the four, *Bound East for Cardiff*, *The Moon of the Caribbees*, and *In the Zone*, was laid aboard the British vessel. Later in 1911 O'Neill signed as an able-bodied seaman aboard the S/S *New York* bound for Southampton and Cherbourg. He resented the patronizing attitude of the passengers toward the "black gang" of firemen and coal passers, and this resentment furnished the theme of *The Hairy Ape*. The S/S *New York* finally docked at Liverpool, and here O'Neill found in a waterfront dive the setting for *The Long Voyage Home*.

Many of O'Neill's plays were produced in London with marked success. Despite this he attracted the unfavorable notice of the critic of the *Times Literary Supplement*, who could find merit in only two out of the twenty-nine plays published in London. His opinion was quite evidently not shared by the British playgoer.

We have even exchanged writers with Britain. T. S. Eliot, a towering figure in twentieth-century poetry and drama, resided in England for many years, became a British subject, and died there. In return, W. H. Auden, a native Briton and an outstanding poet, has come to America to live and has become a naturalized citizen of the United States.

An expatriate poet who chose to live in England and on the Continent was Ezra Pound, who exercised a great influence on the young poets of his time, both English and American, notably T. S. Eliot. He is perhaps best known for his *Cantos*, published over a period of years.

As a final example of Anglo-American cultural exchange there is Robert Frost. Frost found himself as a poet in England. He went there when he was nearing forty, and under the influence of a group of British poets he buckled down to the task of organizing his poems into two slender volumes, *A Boy's Will* (1913) and *North of Boston* (1914). After publication in London, these books quickly crossed the Atlantic, and on both sides of the water Frost found his reputation established as a major American poet. Frost revisited England twice during later life, the last time to receive honorary doctorates from Oxford, Cambridge, and Dublin, the only American writer ever to be accorded this triple recognition. Many will remember his poetic tribute to the American dream which he recited at the inaugural of President John Fitzgerald Kennedy in 1961:

The Gift Outright

The land was ours before we were the land's.
She was our land more than a hundred years
Before we were her people. She was ours
In Massachusetts, in Virginia,
But we were England's, still colonials,
Possessing what we still were unpossessed by,
Possessed by what we now no more possessed.
Something we were withholding made us weak
Until we found out that it was ourselves
We were withholding from our land of living,
And forthwith found salvation in surrender.
Such as we were we gave ourselves outright
(The deed of gift was many deeds of war)
To the land vaguely realizing westward,
But still unstoried, artless, unenhanced,
Such as she was, such as she would become.

C. Waller Barrett
Arcadia
Charlottesville, Virginia
1969

Catalogue of the Exhibit

HUGH HENRY BRACKENRIDGE (1748–1816)

A native of Scotland, Brackenridge was brought to America at the age of five. He was educated at Princeton. Among his classmates were James Madison and Philip Freneau. He was the author of the first really important American novel, *Modern Chivalry*.

1   *A Poem, on the Rising Glory of America.* [anon.] Philadelphia: printed by Joseph Crukshank, for R. Aitken, 1772.
First edition. Written in collaboration with Philip Freneau.

2   *The Battle of Bunkers-Hill. A Dramatic Piece, of Five Acts, in Heroic Measure.* [anon.] By a Gentleman of Maryland. Philadelphia: printed and sold by Robert Bell, 1776.
First edition.

3   *The Death of General Montgomery, at the Siege of Quebec. A Tragedy* . . . By the Author of a Dramatic Piece on the Battle of Bunker's-Hill. Philadelphia: printed and sold by Robert Bell, 1777.
First edition.

FRANCIS HOPKINSON (1737–1791)

4 *A Pretty Story Written in the Year of Our Lord 2774.* By Peter Grievous, Esq; A. B. C. D. E. [pseud.]. The Second Edition. Philadelphia: printed and sold by John Dunlap, 1774.

Second edition. The first edition was published earlier in the same year.

WILLIAM HILL BROWN (1765–1793)

5 *The Power of Sympathy: or, The Triumph of Nature. Founded in Truth.* [anon.] Printed at Boston, by Isaiah Thomas and Company, 1789.

First edition. Two copies shown. One is the only known copy in original boards, uncut. The other is the only known presentation copy from William Hill Brown. Inscription in volume one in the author's hand: "Mr. Wm. P. Jones. from his friend & humble Servant The Author." Inscription in volume two, presumably in the recipient's hand: "Wm. H. Brown to Wm. P. Jones."

The authorship was formerly ascribed to the Boston poetess Sarah Wentworth Morton for the unlikely reason that an episode in the novel is based on certain unsavory incidents of her married life. This gave Mrs. Morton a vicarious fame in American literature which lingered until 1894, when it was demonstrated that the real author was William Hill Brown.

6　*The Father; or, American Shandy-ism. A Comedy.* [anon.] New York: printed by Hodge, Allen & Campbell, 1789.

First edition. A revised version entitled *The Father of an Only Child* was published in London in 1807.

7　*Andre; A Tragedy, in Five Acts.* New-York: printed by T. & J. Swords, 1798.

First edition. It was published in London the following year.

8　*Thirty Years Ago; or The Memoirs of a Water Drinker.* New-York: Bancroft & Holley, 1836.

First edition.

ROYALL TYLER (1757–1826)

Born in Boston, educated at Harvard, Tyler made his reputation in Vermont. He was the author of *The Contrast*, a comedy first staged in New York in 1787. The contrast was provided by the principal characters, Dimple, "an imitator of British affectations," and "Colonel Manley, a bluff, outspoken American officer and gentleman." Tyler's novel, *The Algerine Captive*, was republished in London in 1802.

9   *The Contrast, A Comedy; in Five Acts:* Written by a Citizen of the United States. Philadelphia: from the Press of Prichard & Hall, 1790.

First edition.

10   *The Algerine Captive; or, The Life and Adventures of Doctor Updike Underhill* [pseud.]. Printed at Walpole, Newhampshire, by David Carlisle, Jun., 1797.

First edition.

11   *The Yankey in London, Being the First Part of a Series of Letters* Written by an American Youth, during Nine Months' Residence in the City of London; Volume I. [anon.] New-York: printed and published by Isaac Riley, 1809.

First edition. No more published.

SUSAN (SUSANNA HASWELL) ROWSON
(*ca.*1762–1824)

Born in England, Mrs. Rowson was brought to America by her parents at the age of five. She became a leading novelist, the author of *Charlotte*, later known as *Charlotte Temple*. The vitality of this novel is attested by the fact that it has gone through more than 200 editions and is still in print.

12   *Charlotte. A Tale of Truth.* London: printed for William Lane, at the Minerva, 1791.

First edition. The only known copy. See illustration.

13   *Charlotte. A Tale of Truth.* Philadelphia: printed by D. Humphreys, 1794.

First American edition.

14   *Mentoria; or The Young Lady's Friend.* London: printed for William Lane, at the Minerva, [1791].

Presentation copy. The inscription is probably not in the author's hand, but presumably in the recipient's: "M: Thomas.   The Gift of the Author   July. 1790." The date of the inscription is incorrect, for the advertisements at the end of volume two quote a review from the *Critical Review* for May, 1791.

15   *The Fille de Chambre.* Dublin: printed by Brett Smith, 1793.

First published as *Rebecca, or, The Fille de Chambre* (London, 1792), but no copy of this edition is known. The copy shown is the earliest edition for which a copy is known. The first American edition was published in Philadelphia in 1794.

16   *Charlotte's Daughter: or, The Three Orphans.* Boston: Richardson & Lord, 1828.

First edition.

CHARLOTTE.

A TALE OF TRUTH.

IN TWO VOLUMES.

She was her parent's only joy;
They had but one—one darling child.
ROMEO AND JULIET.

Her form was faultlefs, and her mind,
Untainted yet by art,
Was noble, juft, humane, and kind,
And virtue warm'd her heart.
But ah! the cruel fpoiler came——

VOL. I.

LONDON:
PRINTED FOR WILLIAM LANE,
AT THE
Minerva,
LEADENHALL-STREET.
M.DCC.XCI.

A unique English copy of the first American best seller
(no. 12)

17   Poetry published in *A Present for Young Ladies*. Boston, 1811.

Autograph manuscript. 35 pp.

18   Two water-color miniatures of Mrs. Rowson as a young lady.

Artist unknown.

19   Pencil sketch of William Rowson, the novelist's husband, as a young man.

Artist unknown.

GILBERT IMLAY (*ca.*1754–1828?)

A native American, Imlay fought in the Revolution and after that struggle turned up in Kentucky, where, presumably, he wrote *The Emigrants*, a novel designed among other things "to show the superior merits of the Social organization in the United States to that of Great Britain." This novel is one of the rarest in American literature.

20   *The Emigrants, &c. or The History of an Expatriated Family, Being a Delineation of English Manners, Drawn from Real Characters.* Written in America. London: printed for A. Hamilton, 1793.

First edition.

ANONYMOUS

21   *The History of Constantius & Pulchera, or Constancy Rewarded: An American Novel.* Printed at Boston, 1794.

First edition. Only known copy with this date. Others are dated 1795.

22   *Amelia; or, The Faithless Briton. An Original American Novel.* Boston: printed for and sold by W. Spotswood and C. P. Wayne, 1798.

First edition.

ANN ELIZA BLEECKER (1752–1783)

Known principally as a poet, Mrs. Bleecker was the author of a novel, *The History of Maria Kittle*, the story of which is laid during the French and Indian War although it is largely based on Mrs. Bleecker's experiences during the advance of Gentleman Johnny Burgoyne's army.

23 *The History of Maria Kittle. In a Letter to Miss Ten Eyck.* Hartford: printed by Elisha Babcock, 1797.

First edition.

JAMES BUTLER (1755?–1842)

24   *Fortune's Foot-Ball: or, The Adventures of Mercutio. Founded on Matters of Fact.* Harrisburgh, Pennsylvania: printed by John Wyeth, 1797–98.

First edition. The novel is "a wild tale of an English gentleman who, after losing a fiancée by death and a mistress by a cannon ball from a pirate ship, is pressed by a British ship and reaches Quebec but never touches the United States. The author pauses twice in the novel to denounce British tyranny toward America."

CHARLES BROCKDEN BROWN (1771–1810)

25 *Wieland; or The Transformation. An American Tale.* [anon.] New-York: printed by T. & J. Swords, 1798.

First edition. This is Chancellor James Kent's copy with his signature on the title page. The first English edition was published in London in 1811.

26 *Arthur Mervyn; or, Memoirs of the Year 1793.* By the Author of Wieland [etc.]. Philadelphia: printed and published by H. Maxwell, 1799.

First edition.

27 *Arthur Mervyn; or, Memoirs of the Year 1793.* Second Part. By the Author of Wieland [etc.]. New-York: printed and sold by George F. Hopkins, 1800.

First edition.

28 *Arthur Mervyn. A Tale.* London: printed at the Minerva-Press, 1803.

First English edition.

29 *Edgar Huntly; or, Memoirs of a Sleep-Walker.* By the Author of Arthur Mervyn [etc.]. Philadelphia: printed by H. Maxwell, 1799.

First edition.

30 *Edgar Huntly, or Memoirs of a Sleep-Walker. A Novel.* London: printed at the Minerva-Press, 1803.

First English edition.

31 *Ormond; or The Secret Witness.* By the Author of Wieland, Arthur Mervyn, &c. &c. London: printed at the Minerva-Press, 1800.

First English edition.

Bryant made six trips to England and Europe and planned to settle there with his family. He returned to New York, however, to revive the dying New York *Evening Post* and remained with that paper the rest of his life.

32 *The Embargo, or Sketches of the Times; A Satire.* [anon.] By a Youth of Thirteen. Boston: printed for the purchasers, 1808.

First edition of Bryant's first published work. The signature of Edward Sprague Rand, a prominent merchant of Newburyport, Massachusetts, is on the title page. The poem was anti-Jeffersonian and typical of the feelings in New England at the time.

33 *Poems.* Cambridge: printed by Hilliard and Metcalf, 1821.

First edition. One of two known copies in the original wrappers. The book contains *Thanatopsis*, which brought recognition to Bryant when it was first published in 1817 in the *North American Review*.

34 *Poems.* London: J. Andrews, 1832.

Edited with an introduction by Washington Irving. This is the first edition of Bryant's collected poetry to appear in England.

35 *A Discourse on the Life and Genius of James Fenimore Cooper.* Delivered in Metropolitan Hall New York on Wednesday the 25th of February. (A memorial tribute.)

Autograph manuscript. 36 pp. Bryant's tribute to Cooper was first published in the New York *Evening Post*, February 26, 1852. First publication in book form occurred in *Memorial of James Fenimore Cooper* (New York, 1852).

JAMES KIRKE PAULDING (1778–1860)

Paulding collaborated with Washington and William Irving in their first literary production, *Salmagundi* (1807–8). "An aggressive patriotism which amounted to Anglophobia" caused him to rejoice "in twisting the lion's tail." This is reflected in such works as:

36   *The Diverting History of John Bull and Brother Jonathan.* By Hector Bull-us [pseud.]. New-York: Inskeep & Bradford, 1812.

First edition.

37   *A Sketch of Old England*, By a New-England Man. [anon.] New-York: Charles Wiley, 1822.

First edition.

38   *John Bull in America; or, The New Munchausen.* [anon.] New-York: Charles Wiley, 1825.

First edition. Uncut, in original boards. The signature of Henry Brevoort, friend of Paulding and Washington Irving, is on the inside front cover.

WASHINGTON IRVING (1783–1859)

39   *The Sketch Book of Geoffrey Crayon, Gent.* [pseud.]. New-York: printed by C. S. Van Winkle, 1819–20.

First edition. In seven parts in original printed wrappers.

40   *A History of New York, From the Beginning of the World to the End of the Dutch Dynasty.* By Diedrich Knickerbocker [pseud.]. London: John Murray, 1821.

First English edition. Presentation copy to the wife of the Irish poet Thomas Moore: "Mrs. Thomas Moore from her sincere friend Washington Irving London July 17th 1824."

41   *Bracebridge Hall; or, The Humorists.* By Geoffrey Crayon, Gent. [pseud.]. London: John Murray, 1822.

First English edition.

42   *The Sketch Book of Geoffrey Crayon.*

Autograph manuscript. 225 pp.

43   *A History of New York.*

Autograph manuscript. 48 pp. Scattered pages.

44   *Bracebridge Hall.*

Autograph manuscript of volume two of the American edition. 353 pp.

45   Three ALS sending manuscript copy of *The Sketch Book* for printing in America.

P.S. any curious document & manuscript connected or modern that you can procure & forward me, would be precious to me, as there is a great curiosity here as to any thing relative to Spain

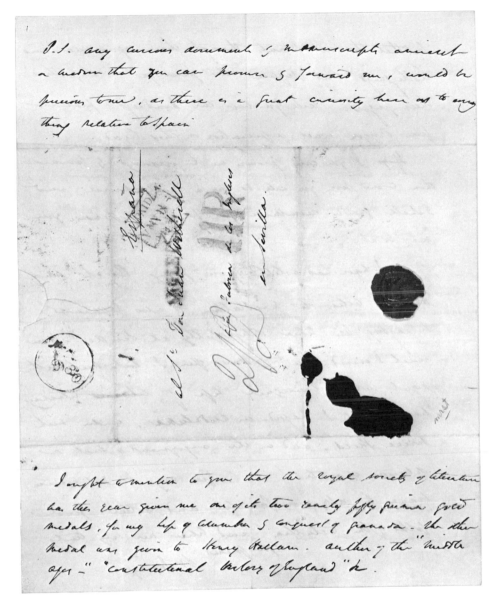

I ought to mention to you that the royal society of literature has this year given me one of its two yearly fifty guinea gold medals, for my life of Columbus & conquest of Granada. The other medal was given to Henry Hallam. author of the "middle ages" "constitutional history of England" &c.

Irving writes of a medal given him (no. 46)

a)   London, April 1, 1819, Irving to his close friend Henry Brevoort, an affluent citizen of New York.

Published in *Life & Letters of Washington Irving*, by Pierce M. Irving, I (New York, 1883), 204.

.   .   .   .   .

I send a second ms. of The Sketch Book. It is not so large as the first but I have not been able to get more matter ready for publication; and indeed I am not particular about the work being regular in any way. The price of this number of course must be less than the first. . . . Let me know what themes etc. would be popular and striking in America; for I have been so long in England that things cease to strike me here as novelties & begin to wear a common place aspect.

b)   London, May 13, 1819, Irving to his brother, John Treat Irving.

Presumably unpublished.

.   .   .   .   .

By the ship which takes this I forward some mss. for publication, being the third number of an occasional work . . . as I am out of money. I drew because I apprehended I should be out of cash before I could get my writings in course of publication. I hope by the time this arrives some of them may be in print & the question settled whether they are profitable.

c)   London, August 16, 1819, Irving to Henry Brevoort.

Published in *Life & Letters of Washington Irving*, by P. M. Irving, I, 211.

.   .   .   .   .

In great haste I inclose you an essay which I have just scribbled and which I wish inserted in the fourth number in place of one of the articles, as I am afraid the number has too great a predominance of the humorous. You may insert it in place of John Bull: and keep that article for the fifth number. I have not had time to give this article a proper finishing, and wish you to look sharp that there are not blunder and tautologies in it. It has been scribbled off hastily and part of it actually in a church yard on a recent ramble into the country.

46   ALS, May 13, 1830, Irving to Don Juan Wetherell.

Presumably unpublished. See illustration.

.   .   .   .   .

I ought to mention to you that the royal society of literature has this year given me one of its two yearly fifty guinea gold medals, for my life of Columbus & Conquest of Granada. The other medal was given to Henry Hallam—author of the "Middle Ages"—"Constitutional History of England" etc.

The medal awarded to Irving, obverse and reverse (no. 47)

47   Medal of the Royal Society of Literature presented to
Irving April 3, 1830.

The medal is cast in solid gold. Irving was the first American to receive it. See
illustration.

48   *Rip Van Winkle.*

Six original pen and ink drawings by Felix O. C. Darley. These were published in
Illustrations of "Rip Van Winkle" ([New York], 1848), designed and etched by Darley
for the members of the American Art-Union.

JAMES FENIMORE COOPER (1789–1851)

49 *Precaution, A Novel.* [anon.] New-York: A. T. Goodrich & Co., 1820.

First edition.

50 *The Spy; A Tale of the Neutral Ground.* By the Author of "Precaution." New-York: Wiley & Halsted, 1821.

First edition.
   Also shown is a copy of the third edition (New York, 1822) presented to the author's wife: "Mrs. James Cooper from her affectionate husband the Author."

51 *The Spy; A Tale of the Neutral Ground.* [anon.] London: G. and W. B. Whittaker, 1822.

First English edition.

52 *The Pioneers, or The Sources of the Susquehanna; A Descriptive Tale.* By the Author of "The Spy." London: John Murray, 1823.

First English edition. First of the Leatherstocking series.

53 *The Pilot; A Tale of the Sea.* By the Author of "The Spy," "Pioneers," &c. &c. &c. London: John Miller, 1824.

First English edition. Dramatized as *The Wigwam* and performed in Covent Garden, London, at Easter time, 1830.

54 *The Last of the Mohicans; A Narrative of 1757.* By the Author of "The Spy," "The Pilot," "The Pioneers," &c. &c. London: John Miller, 1826.

First English edition. Published about two months after the American edition.

55 *The Prairie, A Tale,* By the Author of "The Spy," "The Pilot," &c. &c. London: Henry Colburn, 1827.

First edition. Advance sheets from the Paris edition of 1827 were used in the London edition.

56 *Notions of the Americans: Picked Up by a Travelling Bachelor.* [anon.] London: Henry Colburn, 1828.

First edition. Followed by the American edition

57 *The Pathfinder; or, The Inland Sea.* By the Author of "The Pioneers," "The Last of the Mohicans," "The Prairie," Etc. London: Richard Bentley, 1840.

First edition. Followed by the American edition two months later.

58 *The Deerslayer: or, The First War-Path. A Tale.* By the Author of "The Last of the Mohicans," "The Pathfinder," [Etc.]. Philadelphia: Lea & Blanchard, 1841.

First edition? The English edition may have preceded the American. The precise date of publication has not been determined. Formerly owned by Joseph Holt Ingraham and signed by him.

59 *Home As Found.*

Manuscript. 361 pp. Printer's copy for the London edition (1838), in the hand of an amanuensis with extensive revisions in Cooper's hand. Published under the title *Eve Effingham; or, Home.*

60 *The Two Admirals: A Tale.*

Autograph manuscript. 284 pp. First published in 1842, the English edition preceded the American by a month.

61 Early oil portrait of Cooper by Winkler.

Date unknown. See illustration.

62 Water-color miniature of Cooper by W. H. Powell.

63 *The Water-Witch.*

Original pencil sketch by Felix O. C. Darley and the subsequent engraving. Darley was the artist for the illustrated edition of Cooper's works (New York, 1859–61).

An early oil portrait of Cooper (no. 61)

JOHN NEAL (1793–1876)

64   *Randolph, A Novel.* By the Author of Logan—and Seventy-Six. [New York]: published for whom it may concern, 1823.

First edition. In this novel Neal pays his respects to British authors.

65   *Brother Jonathan: or, The New Englanders.* [anon.] William Blackwood, Edinburgh: and T. Cadell, London, 1825.

First edition.

66   *Authorship, A Tale.* By a New Englander Over-Sea. [anon.] Boston: Gray and Bowen, 1830.

First edition.

JOHN HOWARD PAYNE (1791–1852)

67   *Clari; or, The Maid of Milan: An Opera, in Three Acts.*
London: John Miller, 1823.

First edition. *Home! Sweet Home!* appears for the first time.

68   *Home! Sweet Home!* London: Goulding, D'Almaine,
Potter, & Co., [1823].

First edition of this classic in sheet music form. Payne is not credited as author of the
lyrics. See illustration.

69   *Charles the Second; or, The Merry Monarch. A Comedy, in
Three Acts.* London: printed for Longman, Hurst, Rees,
Orme, Brown, and Green, 1824.

First edition. Presentation copy: "J. Fawcett Esqr. with the author's best acknowl-
edgements." Washington Irving collaborated with Payne on the play.

Home! Sweet Home! in sheet music form (no. 68)

LYDIA MARIA CHILD (1802–1880)

Mrs. Child was interested in the novel as history. Her *Letters from New-York* went through eleven editions in seven years.

70   *The Rebels, or Boston before the Revolution.* By the Author of Hobomok. Boston: Cummings, Hilliard, and Company, 1825.

First edition. Dedication copy: "To George Ticknor, Esq. With the best respects of the author."

71   *Letters from New-York.* New-York: Charles S. Francis and Company, 1843.

First edition. Presentation copy: "Mary R. Preston. from her affectionate sister, the Author."

EDGAR ALLAN POE (1809–1849)

72 *Tamerlane and Other Poems.* By a Bostonian. Boston: Calvin F. S. Thomas, Printer, 1827.

First edition of Poe's first book of poetry. In original printed wrappers.

73 *The Murders in the Rue Morgue.* In *The Prose Romances of Edgar A. Poe* . . . Uniform Serial Edition . . . No. 1. Philadelphia: published by William H. Graham, 1843.

First edition. Lacks the printed cover title.

74 *Mesmerism "in Articulo Mortis." An Astounding & Horrifying Narrative, Shewing the Extraordinary Power of Mesmerism in Arresting the Progress of Death.* London: Short & Co., 1846.

First edition. The only book by Poe published first in England.

75 ALS, Philadelphia, June 21, 1841, Poe to Washington Irving.

Published in *Letters of Edgar Allan Poe*, edited by John Ostrom (New York, 1966), pp. 161–63.

Dear Sir,

Mr George R. Graham of this city, and myself, design to establish a Monthly Magazine, upon certain conditions, one of which is the procuring your assistance in the enterprise. Will you pardon me for saying a few words upon the subject?

I need not call your attention to the signs of the times in respect to Magazine literature. You will admit the tendency of the age in this direction. The brief, the terse, the condensed, and the easily circulated will take place of the diffuse, the ponderous, and the inaccessible. Even our Reviews are found too massive for the taste of the day—I do not mean for the taste of the merely uneducated, but also for that of the few. In the meantime the finest minds of Europe are beginning to lend their spirit to Magazines. In this country, unhappily, we have not any journal of the class, which either can afford to offer pecuniary inducement to the highest talent, or which would be, in all respects, a fitting vehicle for its thoughts. In the supply of this deficiency there would be a point gained;

and the project of which I speak has originated in the hope of supplying it.

Mr. Graham is a lawyer, but for some years past has been occupied in publishing. His experience of the business of a periodical is great. He is a gentleman of high social standing, and possessed of ample pecuniary means. You will perhaps remember myself as the original editor of the South: Lit. Messenger, of Richmond, Vª, and I have otherwise had much to do with the editorial conduct of Magazines. Together, we would enter the field with a full understanding of the difficulties to be encountered, and, we hope, with full ability to meet them.

The work will be an octavo of 96 pages. The paper will be of excellent quality—very far superior to that of the N. A. Review. The type will be new (always new) clear and bold, with distinct face. The matter will be disposed in a single column. The printing will be done upon a hand press, in the best manner. There will be a broad margin. We shall have no engravings, except occasional wood-cuts (by Adams) when demanded in obvious illustration of the text; and, when so required, they will be worked in with the type—not upon separate pages, as in "Arcturus." The stitching will be done in the French style, permitting the book to lie fully open. Upon the cover, and throughout, the endeavour will be to preserve the greatest purity of taste, consistent with decision and force. The price will be $5.

The chief feature in the literary department will be that of contributions from the most distinguished pens (of America) *exclusively;* or, if this plan cannot be wholly carried out, we propose, at least, to procure the aid of some five or six of the most distinguished, and to admit *few* articles from other sources—none which are not of a very high order of merit. We shall endeavour to engage the permanent services of yourself, Mr Cooper, Mr Paulding, Mr Kennedy, Mr Longfellow, Mr Bryant, Mr Halleck, Mr Willis, and, perhaps, one or two others. In fact, as before said, our ability to make these arrangements is a condition without which the Magazine will not go into operation; and my immediate object in addressing you now, is to ascertain how far we may look to yourself for aid.

It would be desirable that you agree to furnish one paper each month—either absolute or serial—and of such length as you might deem proper. We leave terms entirely to your own decision. The sums specified would be paid as you might suggest. It would be necessary that an agreement should be made for one year, during which period you should be pledged not to write for any other American magazine. The journal will be commenced on the first of January 1842, and (should we be so fortunate as to obtain your consent to our proposal) it would be best that we should have in hand, by the first of December 1841, at least two of the papers intended for publication, from each contributor.

With this letter I despatch one of similar tenor to each of the gentlemen above named. If you cannot consent to an unconditional reply, will you be

kind enough to say whether you will write for us upon condition that we suc-
ceed in our engagements with the others—specifying what others?

With high respect
Yr ob St
Edgar A Poe

76   Pen and ink drawing of Poe by Édouard Manet.

WILLIAM A. CARUTHERS (*ca.*1800–1846)

77   *The Cavaliers of Virginia, or the Recluse of Jamestown. An Historical Romance of the Old Dominion.* By the Author of "The Kentuckian in New-York." New-York: Harper & Brothers, 1834–35.

First edition.

78   *The Knights of the Horse-Shoe; A Traditionary Tale of the Cocked Hat Gentry in the Old Dominion.* By the Author of the "Cavaliers of Virginia," &c., &c. Wetumpka, Alabama: printed and published by Charles Yancey, 1845.

First edition.

AUGUSTUS BALDWIN LONGSTREET (1790–1870)

Born in Augusta, Georgia, Longstreet was a lawyer and teacher as well as a humorist. His book *Georgia Scenes* is the cornerstone of American frontier humor.

79 *Georgia Scenes, Characters, Incidents, &c. In the First Half Century of the Republic.* By a Native Georgian. Augusta: printed at the S. R. Sentinel office, 1835.

First edition. Thomas Hardy used the story of *The Militia Company Drill* in *The Trumpet-Major*.

WILLIAM GILMORE SIMMS (1806–1870)

80 *The Yemassee. A Romance of Carolina.* By the Author of "Guy Rivers," "Martin Faber," &c. New-York: Harper & Brothers, 1835.

First edition. Colonial South Carolina.

81 *The Partisan: A Tale of the Revolution.* By the Author of "The Yemassee," "Guy Rivers," &c. New-York: Harper & Brothers, 1835.

First edition. The first and probably the best of Simms's Revolutionary War novels.

82 *The Wigwam and the Cabin.* By the Author of "The Yemassee," "Guy Rivers," &c. First Series. London: Wiley & Putnam, 1845.

First English edition. Sheets of the first American edition with the London title page.

83 *The Wigwam and the Cabin* . . . Second Series. London: Wiley & Putnam, 1846.

First English edition. Sheets of the first American edition with the London title page.

84 *A Supplement to the Plays of William Shakspeare.* New York: George F. Cooledge & Brother, 1848.

First edition. Edited with an introduction by Simms, this is the first American edition of seven plays once attributed to Shakespeare

HENRY WADSWORTH LONGFELLOW (1807–1882)

85 *Outre-Mer: or, A Pilgrimage to the Old World.* By an American. London: Richard Bentley, 1835.

First English edition. Presentation copy: "George S. Hillard from his friend the Author. Cambridge. June 25. 1840."

86 *The Song of Hiawatha.* London: David Bogue, 1855.

First edition. The English edition preceded the American edition by several days.

87 *The Courtship of Miles Standish, and Other Poems.* London: W. Kent & Co., 1858.

First edition. The English edition preceded the American.

88 *The Courtship of Miles Standish, and Other Poems.* Boston: Ticknor and Fields, 1858.

First American edition. Presentation copy: "From the Author. 1858," with the signature of Longfellow's sister, Annie L. Pierce, on the facing blank leaf.

89 *Michael Angelo.* [Part II.] London, 1882.

Copyright printing. The first published edition appeared with a Cambridge, Mass., 1884 imprint. The present copy is bound with Parts I and III as published in issues of the *Atlantic Monthly* for January and March of 1883.

90 *Sonnet* (to Tennyson).

Autograph manuscript signed. 1 p. Accompanied by James T. Fields's card with a note in Fields's hand presenting the manuscript to Miss Waring: "For Miss Waring, from J. T. F. Longfellow's Sonnet to Tennyson, in the handwriting of the author." See illustration.

Poet,! I come to touch thy lance with mine;
  Not, as a Knight, who on the listed field
  Of tourney touched his adversary's shield
  In token of defiance, but in sign
Of homage to the mastery, which is thine
  In English song; nor will I keep concealed
  And voiceless as a river frost-congealed.
  My admiration for thy verse divine.

Not of the howling Dervishes of song,
  Who wrap the brain with their delirious dance,
  Art thou, O sweet historian of the heart!
Therefore, to thee the laurel leaves belong,
  To thee our love and our allegiance,
  For thy allegiance to the poet's art.

                  Henry W. Longfellow.

Longfellow's *Sonnet* to Tennyson (no. 90)

91 ALS, Portland, March 18, 1835, Longfellow to William Goddard, a friend of Longfellow's wife.

Published in *Letters of Henry Wadsworth Longfellow*, edited by Andrew R. Hilen, Jr., I (Cambridge, Mass., 1966), 478–79.

My dear Sir,

Yr. favor of the 16 reached me yesterday. I agree with you entirely in thinking, that it will be best to take the packet of the 16th. We shall be less hurried—have a pleasanter time—and after all reach London about as soon. If you can find time to write to New York soon, we can doubtless have our choice of state-rooms.

As to the price of passage never varying, I think you must have been misinformed. When Mr. Preble of this place sailed for London with his family (our Minister to the Netherlands) they made a handsome deduction; so he informed me. Another friend of mine sailed for Havre with his wife some years ago; they put their passage at one hundred each. However, I do not wish to put yr. friend to any inconvenience on this head. It might not be amiss to suggest such a thing; though I by no means wish to urge it.

We shall remain a few days longer with our friends in Portland; and start for yr. city on Tuesday next—should the weather be pleasant. Otherwise, on Wednesday or Thursday.

With kind regards to all yr. family

Very sincerely yours
Henry W. Longfellow

P.S. Will Mary Caroline have the goodness to call upon Miss Crowninshield and inform her of the change in our arrangements and the reasons therefor?

92 ALS, "On board the steamer from Rotterdam to Cologne, on the Rhine," Friday December 4, 1835, Longfellow to William W. Goddard.

Published in *Letters*, ed. Hilen, I, 528–29.

My dear Sir,

I write you these few lines to communicate to you and to my other friends in Boston the mournful intelligence of my dear Mary's death. She expired on Sunday morning Nov. 29. at Rotterdam, in peace and perfect resignation; in her death as in her life mindful more of others than herself, and saying, among the latest words she uttered, "Tell my dear friends at home, that I thought of them at the last hour." Her death was occasioned by extreme debility—the effect of a *miscarriage*, which took place in Amsterdam, on the 1st of October. Three weeks afterwards, on reaching Rotterdam, she had a relapse, which has terminated fatally. For the particulars of her sickness and death, I refer you to my letter to her father, and to Clara's letters.

I have had her body embalmed—inclosed in a leaden coffin, and that again in an oaken one—and the whole put into a case, and directed to yr. care. It will leave Rotterdam on Wednesday next, by the *Brig Elizabeth, Capt. Long*. Have the goodness to pay the charges; and to have the body deposited, *encased as it now is* in the *Tomb of the Mount Auburn Cemetery*. I have heard there is such a tomb for the safe-keeping of bodies, until such a time as preparations for their final burial can be made. On my return I shall purchase a spot in Mount Auburn for a tomb. Let me hear by letter of the safe arrival of the body—By the same vessel I send two trunks containing her clothes; and some things of my own. I do not wish these to be opened until my return, unless it be necessary to open them at the Custom house, which I can hardly think will be the case, under the present circumstances. If it is thought necessary, you will find the key of the large trunk tied to one of the handles; the small trunk is not locked. Have the kindness to take charge of these, until I return to Boston. I do not wish to have them sent to Portland.

This affliction has been very sudden and unexpected by me. Till the last day —and almost till the last hour I cheered myself with vain hopes. And even now I ask myself if it can indeed be true, that she is dead. It seems to me as if we were separated but for a short season, and were soon to meet again. Indeed, I know and feel that such is the case. It gives me a melancholy pleasure to recall the goodness of her life and the calmness of her death; and to think that she is far happier now than we, who have been left behind her. So that I do not mourn as those who are without hope; but think of those words, which *she* loved to repeat in her last sickness:—

> "Father! I thank thee! May no thought
> E'er deem thy chastisements severe;
> But may this heart by sorrow taught,
> Calm each wild wish—each idle fear."

With my affectionate regards to all, I remain

Very truly yr. friend
Henry W. Longfellow

93 ALS, Heidelberg, January 10, 1836, Longfellow to Richard Bentley, a British publisher.

Published in *Letters*, ed. Hilen, I, 535.

Dear Sir,

I have not had the pleasure of hearing from you since I left London, though I wrote to you both from Stockholm and Copenhagen.

I have seen from time to time the flattering notices of Outre Mer, which have appeared in the London periodicals; and I hope that the success of the work has equalled your expectations.

With me some painful circumstances have occurred since I saw you. The long illness of my wife, which terminated in death, and at home the sudden death of the person, upon whom I relied for my travelling expenses— have thrown my financial arrangements into confusion. I mention this, hoping that it may be in your power to send me something from the profits of my book.

Have the goodness to write me immediately; and if you can send me a copy of Outre Mer, through Perthes & Besser, Hamburg, or by private hand to this place, where I shall remain for some months, I shall be obliged to you.

Respectfully yours
Henry W. Longfellow

Richard Bentley Esq
   London

RALPH WALDO EMERSON (1803–1882)

94 *Nature*. [anon.] Boston: James Munroe and Company, 1836.

First edition of the author's first book. Presentation copy: "Mrs. R. Emerson from her affectionate son, R. W. E."

95 *An Oration, Delivered before the Phi Beta Kappa Society, at Cambridge, August 31, 1837*. Second edition. Boston: James Monroe and Company, 1838.

Presentation copy from Thomas Carlyle: "Thomas Erskine Esq T.C." The *Oration's* first appearance in England was under the title *Man Thinking* (1844). It is also known in America as *The American Scholar*, the title under which the first edition was published

96 *Orations, Lectures, and Addresses*. London: H. G. Clarke and Co., 1844.

Many of Emerson's addresses appeared in book form first in London, including the 1837 Phi Beta Kappa address.

97 *Nature; An Essay. And Lectures on the Times*. London: H. G. Clarke and Co., 1844.

First edition. First appearance of *Introductory Lecture*, *The Conservative*, and *The Transcendentalist*.

98 *Essays*. Second Series. London: John Chapman, 1845.

First English edition.

99 *Poems*. London: Chapman, Brothers, 1847.

First edition. The English edition preceded the American. Publisher's presentation copy: "Ferdinand Freiligrath Esq with the Publisher's Compliments."

100　*English Traits.* Boston: Phillips, Sampson, and Company, 1856.

First edition. A page of "additional Errata" in Emerson's hand is tipped in.

101　*Tribute to Walter Scott, on the One Hundredth Anniversary of His Birthday, by the Massachusetts Historical Society, August 15, 1871.* Boston: privately reprinted from the Proceedings of the Society, 1872.

Emerson's remarks are included on pages 6–8.

102　*Hymn　Sung at the Completion of the Concord Monument, April 19, 1836.*

Autograph manuscript. 1 p. See illustration.

103　ALS, September 15, 1844, Emerson to John Chapman, a London publisher.

Presumably unpublished. Concerns the publication of his *Essays* in England.

104　ALS, Concord, July 31, 1847, Emerson to Alexander Ireland.

Incompletely printed in Alexander Ireland, *In Memoriam* (London, 1882); pp. 78–79.
　My dear Sir,
　　I owe you hearty thanks for your effective attention to my affair, which was attractive enough to me in the first proposition, and certainly assumes in your hands a feasible shape. I have a good deal of domestic immoveableness—being fastened down by wife & children by books & studies by peartrees & appletrees—but after much hesitation can find no sufficient resistance to this animating invitation and I decide to go to England in the autumn. I think to leave home about the 1 October, perhaps in the steamer, but more probably in the sailing packet which leaves Boston for Liverpool on the 5th of each month;— and, at any rate, shall expect to be in England before the 1 November. From the 1 November, I will take your advice as to the best order of fulfilling those engagements you offer me at Manchester, Sheffield, & Leeds. In regard to the subjects of my lectures, I hope to send you by the next steamer some programme or sketch of programme that may serve a general purpose. I could more easily furnish myself for so "numerous" a course as seems to offer itself if there were any means of preventing your newspaper reporters from publishing such ample

HYMN
Sung at the completion of the Concord Monument
April 19, 1836.

By the rude bridge that arched the flood,
  Their flag to April's breeze unfurled,
Here once the embattled farmers stood,
  And fired the shot heard round the world.

The foe long since in silence slept;
  Alike the conqueror silent sleeps;
And Time the ruined bridge has swept
  Down the dark stream which seaward creeps.

On this green bank, by this soft stream,
  We set today a votive stone;
That memory may their deed redeem
  When, like our sires, our sons are gone.

Spirit, that made those heroes dare
  To die, and leave their children free,
Bid Time and Nature gently spare
  The shaft we raise to them and thee.

R. Waldo Emerson.

Manuscript of one of Emerson's poems (no. 102)

transcripts as I notice (in the "Examiners" you were so good as to send me—) of Mr Marston's Lectures. But I will see what I have to say.

Meantime, I beg you not to give yourself any farther pains in this matter which I fear has already cost you much. It will give me pleasure to speak to bodies of your English people, but I am sure it will give me much more to meet with yourself & other honoured individuals in private: and I see well, that, if there were no lecturing, I should not fail to find a solid benefit in the visit. I write a note of reply to Mr Hudson, to go with this.

With great regard, Your friend & servant,

[Signature cut out]

NATHANIEL PARKER WILLIS (1806–1867)

105 *Tortesa the Usurer. A Play.* New-York: published by Samuel Colman, No. 8 Astor House, 1839.

First edition. Described by Poe as "by far the best play from the hand of an American author."

106 *Paul Fane; or, Parts of a Life Else Untold. A Novel.* New York: C. Scribner. Boston: A. Williams & Co. London: Sampson Low, Son & Co., 1857.

First edition (second imprint noted by Wright).

HENRY WILLIAM HERBERT (1807–1858)
(FRANK FORESTER)

Herbert, grandson of the first Earl of Carnarvon, was born in London and educated at Eton and Cambridge. In 1831 he came to the United States and lived here for the rest of his life. He never forgot his aristocratic ancestors and often sported cavalier boots and King Charles spurs. He was the author of numerous Anglo-American sporting books and novels under the pseudonym Frank Forester.

107   *The Warwick Woodlands, or Things as They Were There, Ten Years Ago*, By Frank Forester. Philadelphia: G. B. Zieber & Co., 1845.

First editon.

108   *Field Sports in the United States, and the British Provinces of America*. By Frank Forester. London: Richard Bentley, 1848.

First edition.

JAMES RUSSELL LOWELL (1819–1891)

109 *Conversations on Some of the Old Poets.* Cambridge, [Massachusetts]: published by John Owen, 1845.

First edition. In original printed wrappers. This was Celia Thaxter's copy and has her signature and date (January, 1845). The book contains Lowell's essays on British writers.

110 *The Cathedral.* Boston: Fields, Osgood, & Co., 1870.

First edition. Presentation copy: "To Robert Browning, with an appreciation heightening for thirty years, from the Author. 30th Decr 1889."

111 *My Study Windows.* Boston: James R. Osgood and Company, 1871.

First edition. Presentation copy: "To W. D. Howells, with the author's love, 30th Jan^y—1871."

112 *Transactions of the Wordsworth Society.* No. VI. [Edinburgh: T. & A. Constable, 1888.]

First edition. Presentation copy: "To Mrs. G. W. Smalley with the affectionate regards of the Author." The book contains Lowell's presidential address before the society.

113 *American Ideas for English Readers.* Boston: J. G. Cupples Co., [cop. 1892].

First edition. Introduction by Henry Stone. An unauthorized publication of speeches made in England.

114 *Class Poem*

Autograph manuscript. 22 pp. See illustration. The following excerpt is from Note 7, pages 2 and 3 of the manuscript:

The day has long past when any one would think of ridiculing Wordsworth. As Carlyle says of Fichte, "What is the wit of a thousand wits to him? The cry of a thousand choughs assaulting that old cliff of granite?" But his fame as a poet does not rest on Peter Bells, (though it contains passages as beautiful as almost any in the language) nor on any of his "Nursery" poetry, as it has been termed. A man may be a great genius & yet be mistaken, & so apparently Wordsworth thought himself, for he gradually shook off the style of his younger poetry. He probably saw that what was silly in prose no verse would ever make wiser.

And yet we have floods of verses with *all* the childishness & none of the redeeming points of Wordsworth's earlier style. For instance, Tennyson's "Oh darling Room!" of which one verse will be a sufficient specimen

"Oh darling room, my hearts delight,
Dear room, the apple of my sight,
With thy two couches soft & white,
There is no room so exquisite,
No little room so warm & bright,
Wherein to read, wherein to write."

The four last lines are considered "so exquisite" that they are repeated in the course of the piece. Some men seem to think, to use Byron's words,

"That Christmas stories tortured into rhyme
Contain the essence of the true sublime."—

115   ALS, London, January 5, 1884, Lowell to William Gladstone.

Presumably unpublished. Concerns *The Minister's Wooing* and Harriet Beecher Stowe.

HERMAN MELVILLE (1819–1891)

116 *Narrative of a Four Months' Residence among the Natives of a Valley of the Marquesas Islands; or, A Peep at Polynesian Life.* London: John Murray, 1846.

First edition. In original paper wrappers. The American edition was entitled *Typee*.

117 *Typee: A Peep at Polynesian Life. During a Four Months' Residence in a Valley of the Marquesas.* New York: Wiley and Putnam. London: John Murray, 1846.

First American edition. In original paper wrappers.

118 *The Story of Toby, A Sequel to "Typee."* By the Author of That Work. London: John Murray, [1846].

First English edition. In original wrappers. One of two known copies. See illustration.

119 *Omoo: A Narrative of Adventures in the South Seas; Being a Sequel to the "Residence in the Marquesas Islands."* London: John Murray, 1847.

First English edition. In original paper wrappers.

120 *Mardi: And a Voyage Thither.* London: Richard Bentley, 1849.

First English edition.

121 *White Jacket; or, The World in a Man-of-War.* London: Richard Bentley, 1850.

First English edition.

MURRAY'S
HOME AND COLONIAL LIBRARY.

THE STORY OF TOBY,

A SEQUEL TO "TYPEE."

BY THE AUTHOR OF THAT WORK.

1846

LONDON:

JOHN MURRAY, ALBEMARLE STREET.

Price Threepence.

W. CLOWES AND SONS,   STAMFORD STREET.

The first English edition of *The Story of Toby* (no. 118)

122   *The Whale.* London: Richard Bentley, 1851.

First edition. The English edition preceded the American edition, which was published under the title *Moby-Dick*.

123   *Moby-Dick; or, The Whale.* New York: Harper & Brothers, 1851.

First American edition. Presentation copy: "Dr: Robert Tomes from H Melville Jan: 5th 1852." See illustration.

124   Chase, Owen. *Narrative of the Most Extraordinary and Distressing Shipwreck of the Whale-Ship Essex, of Nantucket; Which Was Attacked and Finally Destroyed by a Large Spermaceti-Whale, in the Pacific Ocean; with an Account of the Unparalleled Sufferings of the Captain and Crew during a Space of Ninety-three Days at Sea, in Open Boats. in the Years 1819 & 1820.* New-York: published by W. B. Gilley, 1821.

The source book of Melville's masterpiece, *Moby-Dick*.

125   *Redburn: His First Voyage. Being the Confessions of a Sailor-Boy.* London: Richard Bentley, 1853.

First English edition.

126   ALS, New York, April 5, 1852, Melville to John Murray, his English publisher.

Presumably unpublished.

Sir:—This will introduce to you my brother-in-law, Mr. Lemuel Shaw of Massachusetts—a son of Chief Justice Shaw—who purposes passing some part of the coming summer in England.

If it shall lie in your power to extend his views of life in your metropolis, & add to the number of the agreeable acquaintences he will be sure to make there I shall duly value such attention.

You will find Mr. Shaw—as a New-Englander and Bostonian—peculiarly ready to appreciate & admire all that you can show him of what is admirable and enjoyable in England.

Very Truly Yours
Herman Melville

MOBY-DICK;

OR,

THE WHALE.

BY

HERMAN MELVILLE,

AUTHOR OF

"TYPEE," "OMOO," "REDBURN," "MARDI," "WHITE-JACKET."

NEW YORK:

HARPER & BROTHERS, PUBLISHERS.

LONDON: RICHARD BENTLEY.

1851.

The only recorded presentation copy of Melville's supreme
achievement (no. 123)

127 ALS, New York, August 10, 1890, Melville to Havelock Ellis.

Presumably unpublished. Possibly Melville's last letter.

Dear Sir:

I have been away from town, a wanderer hardly reachable for a time, so that your letter was long in coming to hand.

And now in ref [er]ence thereto.

My great grandfather on the paternal side was a native of Scotland. On the maternal side, and in the same remove, my progenitor was a native of Holland; and, on that side, the wives were all of like ancestry.

As to any strain of other blood, I am ignorant, except that my paternal grandfather's wife was of Irish Protestant stock.

Very truly yours
Herman Melville

128   *Aesthetic Papers*. Edited by Elizabeth P. Peabody. Boston: the Editor. New York: G. P. Putnam, 1849.

First printing of Thoreau's *Resistance to Civil Government*.

129   *A Week on the Concord and Merrimack Rivers*. Boston and Cambridge: James Munroe and Company. New York: George P. Putnam. Philadelphia: Lindsay and Blackiston. London: John Chapman, 1849.

First edition of the author's first book. Presentation copy. "Alfred Tennyson with the regards of Henry D. Thoreau." Printer's errors on pages 120 and 139 are corrected in the author's hand. Pasted over the imprint is a rectangular printed label which reads: "Imported by John Chapman, 142, Strand, London."

130   *Walden; or, Life in the Woods*. Boston: Ticknor and Fields, 1854.

First edition. Presentation copy: "Cynthia D. Thoreau from her son."

131   [Literary Studies at Harvard], 1835.

Autograph manuscript. 24 pp. Study notes in Thoreau's hand, including quotations from Longfellow, Irving, and Cooper.

132   Map of the Concord and Merrimack rivers.

Drawn in pencil by Thoreau during the trip which preceded publication of his first book.

133   ALS, Castleton, Staten Island, May 11, 1843, Thoreau to his mother, Mrs. Cynthia Thoreau.

Published in *The Correspondence of Henry David Thoreau*, edited by Walter Harding and Carl Bode (New York, 1958), pp. 98–100.

· · · · ·

Dear Mother and Friends at home, We arrived here safely at 10 o'clock on Sunday morning, having had as good a passage as usual, though we ran aground and were detained a couple of hours. . . . At length we curtseyed up to a wharf just the other side of their Castle Garden. . . . I believe my vacant look, absolutely inaccessible to questions did at length satisfy an army of starving cabmen. . . .

I am 7½ miles from New York, and as it would take half a day at least have not been there yet. I have already run over no small part of the island, to the highest hill and some way along the shore. From the hill directly behind the house, I can see New York—Brooklyn—Long Island—the Narrows, through [which] vessels bound to and from all ports of the world swiftly pass.

NATHANIEL HAWTHORNE (1804–1864)

134 *The Scarlet Letter: A Romance.* London, 1851.

First English edition. Published the year after the American edition.

135 *Transformation: or, The Romance of Monte Beni.* London, 1860.

First edition. Anthony Trollope's copy with his bookplate in each volume. The American edition was entitled *The Marble Faun.*

136 *The Marble Faun: or, The Romance of Monte Beni* Boston, 1860.

First American edition. Presentation copy: "E. R. Whipple Esq with the author's compliments Feby 28. 1860."

137 *Our Old Home: A Series of English Sketches.* Boston, 1863.

First edition. Presentation copy: "Mrs. Annie Fields, from her friend, Nath Hawthorne." Mrs. Fields later presented the volume to Henry James, whose signature is on the end paper. James's study of Hawthorne was published in London in 1879.

138 *A Sketch or Two in Warwick.*

Autograph manuscript. 2 pp. Published in *Our Old Home.*

139 *Consular Experiences.*

Autograph manuscript. 39 pp. Published in *Our Old Home.* Related to Hawthorne's consular experiences in Liverpool.

140 ALS, Liverpool, November 11, 1855, Hawthorne to Henry Wadsworth Longfellow.

Presumably unpublished. Written while Hawthorne was U.S. consul.

141   ALS, Liverpool, April 12, 1856, Hawthorne to Henry Wadsworth Longfellow.

Presumably unpublished. See illustration.

Dear Longfellow,

In London, a few evenings ago, I happen[en?]ed to be at Evans's Supper Rooms (a rather rowdyish place, I am afraid, to which I was introduced by Mr. Albert Smith;) and the proprietor introduced himself to me, and expressed a high sense of the honor which my presence did him. He further said that it had been the "dream and romance of his life," to see Emerson, Channing, Longfellow, and, he was kind enough to add, me, sitting together at a table in his rooms! I could not but smile to think of such a party of roisterers drinking whisky toddy or gin and water at one of his tables, smoking pipes or cigars, and listening to a bachanalian catch from his vocalists. The band played "Hail Columbia" 'Yankee Doodle' &c in my honor; and several of your songs were sung; and the proprietor entreated me to lay this "edition de luxe" (as he called it) of his program, [one word illegible] "at your feet." You must certainly go there when you come to London.

I have been in all sorts of parties within the last few weeks; and in every single one of these, your name was spoken with the highest interest and admiration. Your fame is in its fullest blow; the flower cannot open wider. If there is any bliss at all in literary reputation, you ought to feel it at this moment. I am not quite sure that it is a very enjoyable draught; but if you drink it at all, it is best to take it hot, and sweet, and spiced to the utmost. So do come to England this summer.

There is a strong expectation in London that you *are* coming. Several people said so to me, as if they knew it to be a fact. I hope it is; for I want to see you very much, and it will still be years before I meet you on the other side.

With my best regards to Mrs. Longfellow,

Your friend,
Nath¹ Hawthorne

Hawthorne on Longfellow's fame in England (no. 141)

HARRIET (ELIZABETH) BEECHER STOWE
(1811–1896)

142   *Uncle Tom's Cabin.* London, 1852.

First edition with the illustrations by George Cruikshank. In thirteen parts in the original printed wrappers.

143   *Lady Byron Vindicated. A History of the Byron Controversy, from Its Beginning in 1816 to the Present Time.* Boston, 1870.

First edition.

JOHN ESTEN COOKE (1830–1886)

144   *The Virginia Comedians: or, Old Days in the Old Dominion.* [anon.] Edited from the Mss. of C. Effingham, Esq. New York, 1854.

First edition.

145   *Fairfax: or, The Master of Greenway Court. A Chronicle of the Valley of the Shenandoah.* New York, 1868

First edition. Reissued as *Lord Fairfax*. Young George Washington and Lord Fairfax are principal characters.

146   *Out of the Foam. A Novel.* New York, 1871.

First edition. Reissued as *Westbrooke Hall*. England during the Napoleonic Wars.

147   *Her Majesty the Queen. A Novel.* Philadelphia, 1873.

First edition. A romance of the days of Charles I.

WALT(ER) WHITMAN (1819–1892)

148   *Leaves of Grass.* Brooklyn, 1855.

First edition. Two unique copies, one in original boards, the other with the copyright notice written on the verso of the title page in Whitman's hand. The latter is a presentation copy: "R. W. Griswold, from the author," and has a Whitman letter pasted in.

149   *Poems by Walt Whitman.* Edited by William Michael Rossetti. London, 1868.

150   *The Poetry and Prose of Walt Whitman.* New York, 1949.

Edited by Louis Untermeyer. Specially bound in green morocco by Bayntun of Bath, England, with a water-color miniature of Whitman on the front cover.

151   *Leaves of Grass.*

Autograph manuscript. 376 leaves. The earliest surviving manuscript copy.

152   *The Dead Carlyle.*

Autograph manuscript. 3 pp. Colored pencil sketch of Carlyle, tipped in. See illustrations.

153   ALS, Washington, August 13, 1868, Whitman to his mother.

Published in *Letters Written by Walt Whitman to His Mother, 1866–1872,* edited by R. G. Silver (New York, 1936), pp. 58–60.

Dearest mother, your letter has come this morning—I always read it through, & then in the afternoon read it through a second time—every little item is interesting—

—poor Mat, she has indeed had a narrow escape—to think how it might have happened by another hair's breadth—We are having beautiful weather here—quite cool, except in the middle of the day—I am feeling well as usual—nothing special or new in the office—all seems to go on smoothly—Mr. Evarts is here—Ashton has gone to New York for a few days—I have just sent off quite a batch of letters to Hannah.

Saturday 15th—I took a sail down to Alexandria yesterday—it is six or eight miles—you go down in a steamer, something like the Brooklyn ferry boats—&

to-day I have just been out for nearly two hours—so you see I am not confined very closely—We have not much to do in the office—It is beautiful weather again to-day, cool enough, and I feel very well—It is probable that I shall not take my leave of absence for a few weeks yet—I will send you good word—

Sunday forenoon—16th—I am sitting here by myself in the office—it is warm, but pleasant—It is pretty dull here in Washington now that Congress is away

Afternoon—½ past 3—We have had a hot day so far—had a good dinner—good roast beef & apple pie—had company to-dinner—I have come around to the office to sit in quiet awhile, by my big open window—Nice old window—I have spent so many quiet comfortable hours by it, I shall be sorry enough when I leave it—I never get tired looking out, there is river & hills & gardens & trees—can see ten or twelve miles—& boats sailing—I am going up to O'Connors towards 7 o'clock as usual—I am working at my leisure on my little book—I don't know whether I have spoken of it before—in prose—those pieces in the *Galaxy* form portions of it—it is on political & literary subjects—It is a real pleasure to me—the new edition of Leaves of Grass is all ready fixed —so I don't bother with it any more—

Monday forenoon—Aug 17—Well mother I will close up my letter & send it off to-day—I went out to O'Connors as usual last evening & staid till after 11 o'clock—They have got another house & move in about a month—We are all quite busy to-day in the office—Mr. Evarts & Ashton are both here now, & we have to fly around—Well I enjoy it just as well when I am busy during office hours, or rather I like it better—The pleasant weather continues—we need rain—dear mother how are you getting along, & how is the rheumatism?

Love to you & all.
Walt.

154 ALS, Camden, New Jersey, March 6, 1876, Whitman to Abraham (Bram) Stoker, the author of *Dracula*.

Presumably unpublished. The letter is tipped into a made-up booklet of 4 leaves with paper wrappers, with a hand-lettered title. A handwritten introductory note follows:

Walt Whitman and Bram Stoker

In 1868 when William Michael Ros[s]etti brought out his Selected Poems of Walt Whitman, it raised a regular storm in British literary circles. The bitter minded critics of the time absolutely flew at the Poet and his work as watch-dogs do at a ragged beggar. Unfortunately there were passages in the Leaves of Grass which allowed of attacks, and those who did not, or could not, under-stand the broad spirit of the group of poems took samples of detail which were at least deterrent. Doubtless they thought that it was a case for ferocious attack; as from these excerpts it would seem that the book was as offensive to morals as to taste. They did not scruple to give the *ipsissima verba* of the most repug-nant passages.

The Dead Carlyle

Not for his merely literary merit, (though that was great) – not as "maker of books," but as launching into the self-complacent atmosphere of our days a rough rasping, questioning, dislocating agitation and shock, is the man's final value. It is time the English-speaking peoples had some true idea: about the verteber of genius, namely power. As if they must always have it cut and biased to the fashion, like a lady's cloak!

What a needed service he performs! How he shakes our comfortable reading circles with a touch of the old Hebraic anger and prophecy – and indeed it is just the same. Not Isaiah himself more scornful, more threatening: "The crown of pride, the drunkards of Ephraim shall be trodden under feet: And the glorious beauty which is on the head of the fat valley shall be a fading flower." (The word

Whitman on Carlyle's "final value" (no. 152)

Thomas Carlyle

A pencil sketch of Carlyle (no. 152)

In his own University, Bram Stoker tells us, the book was received with homeric laughter; but a quiet study of it caused him to form an opinion diametrically opposite to that which he had been hearing. From that hour he became a lover of Walt Whitman. A few others took the same view and in time quite a little cult was formed with Edward Dowden, Professor of English Literature, at the head. Many a sturdy battle was waged between the Walt-Whitmanites and their opponents; the struggle going on for years.

One militant evening in 1876, at the "Fortnightly Club"—a club of Dublin men who met occasionally for free discussions—a violent, incisive and altogether outrageous attack was made on Walt Whitman which drew forth a most impassioned speech from Edward Dowden. Bram Stoker followed. Together they carried the question. Stoker, excited by the stress of the meeting went home and before he went to bed poured out his heart in a long letter to Walt Whitman. Bye and bye, came the following characteristic letter from the Poet:

'Bram Stoker,

My Dear young man,

Your letters have been most welcome to me—welcome to me as Person, & then as Author—I don't know which most,—you did well to write to me so unconventionally, so fresh, so manly, & so affectionately too. I too hope (though it is not probable) that we shall one day personally meet each other. Meantime I send you my friendship & thanks.

Edward Dowden's letter containing among others your subscription for a copy of my new edition, has just been rec'd. I shall send the books very soon by express in a package to his address. I have just written to E.D.

My physique is entirely shatter'd—doubtless permanently—from paralysis & other ailments. But I am up & dress'd, & get out every day a little—live here quite lonesome, but hearty, & good spirits.

Write to me again.

Walt Whitman

155 *The Holy Bible*. Oxford, n.d.

Whitman's personal copy of the Bible with his signature on the first blank leaf and on the title page, and a note in his hand: "Nov. 23, 1888—Have had this vol. now with me ten years." Among other notations in Whitman's hand is a list of Whitman family births, marriages, and deaths.

156 Caricature of Whitman published by the *Fifth Avenue Journal* in 1872.

Number 18 of the *Journal*'s Men of the Day series. See illustration.

157 Pencil sketch of Whitman by Eastman Johnson.

MEN OF THE DAY.
No. 18.
FROM
"THE FIFTH AVENUE JOURNAL."
A Mirror of Art, Literature and Society.
Published every Wednesday at 27 City Hall Square, New York.

A caricature of Walt Whitman (no. 156)

DELIA BACON (1811–1859)

158   *The Philosophy of the Plays of Shakspere Unfolded.* With a Preface by Nathaniel Hawthorne. Boston, 1857.

First edition.

159   *The Philosophy of the Plays of Shakspere Unfolded.* With a Preface by Nathaniel Hawthorne. London, 1857.

First English edition.

SAMUEL L(ANGHORNE) CLEMENS (1835–1910)
(MARK TWAIN)

160 *The Celebrated Jumping Frog of Calaveras County, and Other Sketches.* New York, 1867.

First edition of Mark Twain's first published book. Presentation copy: "To my mother—the dearest Friend I ever had, & the truest. Mark Twain New York, May 1, 1867." The first English edition was published in London the same year.

161 *The Innocents Abroad. A Book of Travel in Pursuit of Pleasure.* London, [1870].

First English edition of the first half of *Innocents Abroad*, with introduction by Edward P. Hingston.

162 *The New Pilgrim's Progress. A Book of Travel in Pursuit of Pleasure.* London, [1870].

First English edition of the second half of *Innocents Abroad*.

163 *The Adventures of Tom Sawyer.* London, 1876.

First edition.

164 *The Adventures of Tom Sawyer.* Hartford, 1876.

First American edition. The English edition appeared several months earlier. The copy shown is a presentation copy to the daughter of Edwin Booth:

> Some day, Miss Booth, when you (having become acquainted with my many virtues & merits,) shall come to like me as well as I already like you, we two shall be a couple of right good friends. Then you will say, "I do not value this book because it has worth—since that is questionable—but I value it because Mr. C.'s impulse was kindly & honest & I am satisfied that he would have sent me a much better one if he had been able to write it." (And that will be just as true a thing as you ever said—mark my words!)
>
> Truly Yours
> Samuel L. Clemens

Hartford, Apl. 8/77.

165   *The Prince and the Pauper   A Tale for Young People of All Ages.* Boston, 1882.

First edition. This presentation copy was a prepublication gift from Clemens to his mother: "To Mrs. Jane Clemens, Fredonia, N.Y. With the best love of her son The Author. Hartford, Dec. 1881."

166   *Life on the Mississippi.* London, 1883.

First edition. The American edition was published several days later.

167   *Life on the Mississippi.* New York, [1883].

Clemens's copy used in preparing copy for a later edition. The author's autograph corrections and emendations appear on forty-four pages of the book. The half title, title page, and pages 79–122 have been torn out by the author, probably because he did not have room for the needed corrections. On the inside front cover: "Mark Twain. I published this book at my own expense, as an experiment in economy. It cost me fifty-six thousand dollars before the first copy issued from the press. S.L.C. May, 1908."

168   *The Adventures of Huckleberry Finn (Tom Sawyer's Comrade).* London, 1884.

First edition. The American edition was published several days later. Pasted in on the inside front cover is a small slip inscribed: "Read & corrected by S. L. Clemens."

169   *Adventures of Huckleberry Finn (Tom Sawyer's Comrade).* New York, 1885.

First American edition. Presentation copy to General Philip H. Sheridan's two sons: "To the General's boys this book is offered, with the compliments of The Author. New York, March 21, 1885."

170   Prefaces for *Innocents Abroad.*

Autograph manuscripts. 4 pp. and 2 pp., respectively. Two prefaces written by Clemens for the London edition of 1872 published by Routledge.

     To the English Reader.

     A long introductory speech would not become me, a stranger. So I will only say, in offering this revised edition of my book to the English reader, that it is nothing more than a simple record of a pleasure excursion among foreign peoples with whom he is doubtless much better acquainted than I am. I could not have made it learned or profound, if I had tried my best. I have only written of men & things as they seemed to *me:* & so it is very likely that the reader will discover that my vision was often inaccurate. I did not seriously expect anybody to buy the book when it was originally written—& that will account for a good deal of its chirping complacency & freedom from restraint: the idea that nobody is listening, is apt to seduce a body into airing his small thoughts & opinions with a rather juvenile frankness. But no matter now. I have said enough to make the reader understand that I am not offering this work to him as either law or gospel, upon any point, principle, or subject; but only as a trifle to occupy himself with when he has nothing to do & does not wish to whistle.

The naive ecstasies of an innocent on his first voyage, become, in print, a matter of serious concern to a part of the great general world—to-wit, the part which consists of that Innocent himself. Therefore, as nearly unnecessary as this book is, I feel a solicitude about it. Any American likes to see the work of his hands achieve a friendly reception in the mother country, & it is but natural—natural, too, that he should prize its kindly reception there above the same compliment extended by any people other than his own. Our kindred blood & our common language, our kindred religion & political liberty, make us feel nearer to England than to other nations, & render us more desirous of standing well there than with foreign nationalities that are foreign to us in all particulars. So, without any false modesty, or any consciousness of impropriety, I confess to a desire that Englishmen should read my book. That a great many Englishmen have already read it, is a compliment which I mention in this place with what seems to me to be legitimate & justifiable gratification.

Respectfully,
The Author.

Hartford, U.S.,
　July, 1872.

Preface to the English Edition

At the request of Messrs. George Routledge & Sons, I have made a patient & conscientious revision of this book for republication in England, & have weeded out of it nearly, if not quite, all of the most palpable & inexcusable of its blemishes. At the same time I have wrought into almost every chapter additions which cannot fail to augment the attractions of the book, or diminish them. I have done my best to make this revised volume acceptable to the reader; & so, since I am as other men are, it would gratify me indeed to win his good opinion.

Respectfully,
The Author.

Hartford, U. S., July 1872.
[Marginal note] Please use this if it be *possible*—do try hard, anyway. S. L. C. Tear up the other.

171 *Ah, Sin.*

Autograph manuscript. 15 pp. A portion of the play on which Clemens collaborated with Bret Harte. It was written in 1877, a few years before Harte went to Great Britain as U.S. consul in Glasgow. Also shown is a program for a performance of the play in Daly's Fifth Avenue Theatre.

172 *A Tramp Abroad.*

A portion of the autograph manuscript. 149 pp., comprising almost all of chapter XXV and chapters XXVI and XXVII complete.

173 ALS, Hartford, February 13, 1874, Clemens to Charles Kingsley, the British novelist and poet.

Presumably unpublished.

My dear Mr. Kingsley:

Won't you kindly name a day & hour that I may meet you & yours at the station here & bring you up to our house for a few days visit?

Mrs. Clemens is a trifle scared, but no matter. You are neither ferocious nor sanguinary. I asked her what there was to be afraid of, & she said that meeting such a personage as a Canon of Westminster is something like encountering a King or a Colossal Grand Duke. Possibly she thinks a Canon of Westminster is a new & peculiarly destructive sort of artillery. But if you will come, I will protect her. My wife (this long, long time a most appreciative & admiring reader of yours), is very anxious to have the visit, notwithstanding her honest terrors.

Do try to come—& bring all of your family that are with you.

An earlier call to Boston (a dinner to Mr. Wilkie Collins on Monday) has debarred me from the pleasure of meeting you at the Lotos tomorrow night (which invitation only came this moment.) I am so situated that I cannot well be away from home on both occasions.

Mem. The *best* train to come to Hartford by, is the one which leaves New York at 10 AM—but if you'll send me a telegram or a postcard, I'll be on hand at any train you come by.

174 *A Connecticut Yankee at King Arthur's Court.*

An original pen and ink drawing by Dan Beard. This appears on page 512 of the first edition (1889).

175 Galsworthy, John. *Lines Written in the Greeting Book of the Mark Twain Society.*

Autograph manuscript signed, September 2, 1930. 1 p.

A caricature of Mark Twain (no. 176)

176   Caricature of Clemens by "Fudge."

Water color. See illustration.

177   Oil portrait of Clemens in his Oxford robe by Mrs. Edward A. Ward.

See illustration.

Mark Twain in his Oxford robe (no. 177)

JOAQUIN (CINCINNATUS HEINE [HINER]) MILLER
(1839 or 1841–1913)

178   *Specimens.* [Portland, Oregon, 1868.]

First edition of Miller's first book; privately printed for his friends. This is one of two copies known. It belonged to the printer George H. Himes and was specially bound for him.

179   *Joaquin, et Al.,* by Cincinnatus H. Miller. Portland, Oregon, 1869.

First edition. The London edition (1871) contains a new introduction.

180   *Pacific Poems.* London, 1871.

First edition.

181   *Songs of the Sierras.* London, 1871.

First edition. Inscribed by Miller:
    And truly life is little worth,
    Therefore I say look up, therefore
    I say one little star has more
    Bright gold than all the earth of earth.
                Joaquin Miller   London   June 1871

182   *Songs of the Sun-Lands.* London, 1873.

First edition, large paper. Presentation copy: "J. H. L. Leary from the author."

183   *Life amongst the Modocs: Unwritten History.* London, 1873.

First edition.

(FRANCIS) BRET HARTE (1836–1902)

184   *The Heathen Chinee* Illustrated by Joseph Hull. Chicago, 1870.

First edition. Laid in is an autograph manuscript signed by Harte of the last two verses of the poem.

185   *The Luck of Roaring Camp, and Other Sketches.* Boston, 1870.

First edition. The Jerome Kern copy.

186   *That Heathen Chinee and Other Poems Mostly Humorous.* London, [1871].

First edition.

187   *An Episode of Fiddletown and Other Sketches.* London, [1873].

First edition.

188   *Gabriel Conroy. A Novel.* London, [1876].

First edition in bound form. Previously issued in parts.

189   *In the Carquinez Woods.* London, 1883.

First edition. Presentation copy: "M. S. Van de Velde from her friend Bret Harte September 1st 1883." Madame Van de Velde, an author and wife of a member of the Belgian diplomatic service, was a friend of Harte's. The Van de Velde's London house was Harte's second home.

190   *The Heritage of Dedlow Marsh and Other Tales.* London, 1889.

First English edition. It probably precedes the American edition. Presentation copy: "Lady Alfred Paget, from her friend Bret Harte London. Oct. 89."

191 *The Bret Harte Birthday Book.* Compiled by Madame Van de Velde. London, 1892.

Presentation copy: "To The Hon Mrs. Henniker with cordial Xmas greetings, from Bret Harte London, 1892." Florence Henniker, author and president of the Society of Women Journalists, was acquainted with many prominent literary, political, and social figures. Among the more than 300 signatures in the *Birthday Book* are those of Hardy, Kipling, Harte, Doyle, Lang, and Hope.

192 *The Moral and Instructive Ballad of the Good Lord Byron.*
Autograph manuscript. 7 pp.

193 *Lord of Fontenelle.*

Autograph manuscript. 53 pp. This is Harte's only completed work in the field of light opera. It was written in London about 1901 but was never published. For a dramatic work on which Harte collaborated, see no. 171.

194 ALS, Crefeld, Germany, July 17, 1878, Harte to his wife.

Presumably unpublished. Writing upon his arrival in Crefeld, where he had been assigned as U.S. consul, Harte tells of his homesickness and his feeling of helplessness in a foreign country.

195 ALS, Bournemouth Pier, England, September 9, 1882, Harte to his wife.

Published in *The Letters of Bret Harte,* edited by G. B. Harte (Boston, 1926), pp. 211–12.

My dear Nan,

I received the pictures of the children (Ethel and Jessamy,—why didn't you add yourself and the boys?) as a birthday gift. I dare say they are about as fraudulent as most likenesses, but I was struck with the fact that Totty was beginning to take a better likeness than Ethel, and was having more justice done to the delicacy of her face. Everybody thinks all the pictures *charming*, but I think they are most struck by those of Jessamy.

I have yours and the boys two letters and very grateful acknowledgement from "Liza" for her little birthday gift. I was very glad to find you were again in the Adirondacks; it may be dull, but I know it's better for you all than in New York in this weather. Don't come back too *soon*. I would rather you would give yourself more freedom in expense than run risks and have discomforts.

Bret Harte in London (no. 197)

I ran up to London for a day to dine with Osgood. Imagine *who* I found at dinner? Clarence King, Howells, Aldrich, Dr. Martin, John Hay, Booth, Warner—of my dear old friends, and Henry James, Alma Tadema, Conway of the ones I knew here. It was a most wonderful coincidence to find all these men together in London—it would have been most remarkable for New York or Boston. In King and Dr. Martin I went back to the old San Francisco days. In Howells Hay and Aldrich to the first days of my arrival in the East. I was relieved to find that that [*sic*] with, one or two exceptions, all had grown *fat!* Howells is about as round as Jo. Marier and shorter. I felt relieved.

I am steadily progressing with the play. One more act to finish only. I'll write again before the 15th. Love to all!

Frank

P. S. Address as usual to Glasgow.

196   ALS, May 10, 1884, Harte to Robert Browning.

Presumably unpublished. Harte thanks Browning for his letter and sends Browning a copy of an American edition of one of his recent books.

197   Autographed photograph of Harte taken in London.

See illustration.

198   Cartoon of Harte by "Spy" (Sir Leslie Ward).

Number 191 of the Men of the Day series from *Vanity Fair*. See illustration.

A caricature of Bret Harte (no. 198)

199   *Nuggets and Dust Panned Out in California* by Dod Grile [pseud.]. Collected and Loosely Arranged by J. Milton Sloluck. London, [1873].

First edition. Presentation copy: "C. W. Stoddard from A. G. Bierce."

200   *The Fiend's Delight.* By Dod Grile [pseud.]. London, [1873].

First edition. Presentation copy: "F. Marriott Esqr., With compliments of The Author." Also inscribed by Marriott, "13. Oct. 1873."

201   *Cobwebs from an Empty Skull.* By Dod Grile [pseud.]. Illustrated with Engravings by Dalziel Brothers. London, 1874.

Second English edition. Presentation copy: "H. J. M. Sampson, with best regards of the Author." Sampson was the editor of *Fun*, in which these tales were first published.

202   *Tales of Soldiers and Civilians.*

Printer's copy for the first edition (1891). The *Tales* were first published in newspapers, and clippings from these form the text for this item. Extensive holograph corrections and additions, together with the title page and other matter, are all in Bierce's hand.

203   ALS, [London?], Thursday, [1872?], Bierce to Crawford Wilson, a London journalist and friend.

Presumably unpublished.

   My Dear Sir;

      I think I promised (or threatened) to make use of you for house-hunting purposes some day this week, at Hampstead, or there abouts. I shall not, however, have to put you to so base a purpose; as I happened upon some apartments which suit me tolerably well, *and* I could get them for no less than a month— *and* was obliged to go *somewhere* that day. Thanks for your kind offer of assistance. It would give me much pleasure to receive a call from you. You can drop in *any* evening, as I am always at home after the chickens have gone to roost. (You will say this is throwing away fine opportunities for acquiring poultry, but it does'nt matter.)

Permit me to tell you where I live; it may be a help to you in finding me: 17 Bernard-st., Russell Square, W. C.

Very truly thine
A. G. Bierce

P.S. A black bottle kept.

HENRY JAMES (1843–1916)

After a devout, excited pilgrimage to England and Europe in 1869, James arrived at the momentous decision in 1875 that his best hopes for his future as a literary artist lay in Europe, and in 1876 he settled permanently in England. His greatest theme and one that he returned to again and again was that of the American facing the culture and traditions of the old world. *A Passionate Pilgrim*, the title tale in his first book, concerned an American seeking an ancestral estate in England. He went on to the successful *Daisy Miller* (1879), which depicts an unsophisticated, coquettish, strong-willed girl whose desire to show her independence of convention leads to her tragic death. With the American girl, Isabel Archer, in *The Portrait of a Lady* (1882), James perhaps created his best character. In the much later *Ambassador* (1903), the hero from Massachusetts finds in Europe the fuller and richer life he had been subconsciously seeking.

204   *A Passionate Pilgrim, and Other Tales.* Boston, 1875.
First edition of James's first book.

205   *The Europeans. A Sketch.* London, 1878.
First edition. Presentation copy: "Mrs. Smalley   With cordial regards of H. James Jr.   Oct. 3d 1878."

206   *The Europeans. A Sketch.* Boston, 1879.
First American edition. Presentation copy: "Mrs. Hame with cordial regards of The Author."

207   *Daisy Miller   A Study.* New York, 1879.
First edition.

A pencil sketch of Henry James by Max Beerbohm (no. 217)

208 *The Portrait of a Lady*. London, 1882.

James's own copy with his signature on the half-title page.

209 *The Portrait of a Lady*. Boston, 1882.

First American edition.

210 *The Author of Beltraffio*. Boston, 1885.

First edition. Presentation copy: "Robert Louis Stevenson from his friend, of many evenings, Henry James." Stevenson's calling card is pasted in.

211 *Essays in London and Elsewhere*. New York, 1893.

First edition.

212 *The Ambassadors*. London, 1903.

Presentation copy: "To H. B. Marriott Watson Henry James."

213 ALS, February 13, [1877], James to James Osgood, James's American publisher.

Presumably unpublished.

Dear Mr. Osgood—

Send herewith all of the rest of the copy for the *American* that I have the material for in my hands. (It goes in 2 packets.) The last you shall have as soon [as] I have rec'd. advance sheets of the numbers still to be published. In writing a few days since I said that I did not expect to see proof myself: but I should extremely like to have it sent to my father, living in Cambridge, for final revision. Will you be so good as to give positive orders that this be done? With all hopes for the book's prosperity

Yours very truly
H. James

214 ALS, Venice, June 22, 1907, James to Mrs. Humphry Ward, an English novelist.

Presumably unpublished. Concerns *The American Scene*.

Dear Mrs. Ward—

How kind your gentle & excellent words about The American Scene!— which demanded really no words at all, abounding quite sufficiently as I fear it does itself in that commodity. Yet I do "love" to know, as they say to-day,

To Henry James
_____

Say, indefatiguable alchemist,
Melts not the very moral of your scene,
Curls it not off in vapour from between
Those lips that labour with conspicuous twist?
Your fine eyes, blurred like arc-lamps in a
                                          ⌊mist,
Immensely glare; yet glimmerings intervene
So that your May-Be and your Might-Have-Been
Leave us still plunging for your genuine gist.

How different from Sir Arthur Conan Doyle—
As clear as water and as smooth as oil,
And no jot knowing of what Maisie knew!
Flushed with the sunset air of roseate Rye,
You stand, marmoreal darling of the Few,
Lord of the troubled Speech and single Eye.

Odd-numbered lines: M B
Even-numbered lines: E G

For Mrs Seymour Trower
                    September 6, 1908
        Price: One penny!

A sonnet to Henry James (no. 218)

that the book touched in you at all the chord of interest—it was a very difficult job to perpetrate, every way, & a projected sequel has proved so difficult that I find I have given it up altogether. Coming abroad for as many weeks as I have lately been spending (in Paris, Rome &c) doesnt, moreover make for the retention of American impression—in the *immediately* reproducible way at least. However I am facing homeward impatiently—with only a short very hot & very sweet pause here; & I shall be within nearer hail of you before long. I am never in my life coming abroad again which will make for our [illegible] more closely foregathering. You allude to matters of which I want much to hear more, to hear everything—& I shall knock at your door for that purpose. If you are enjoying the terrible London of June I hope it means you are conveniently well; for myself I fear I have really lingered in Italy partly to let it pass. I greet you all affectionately. & am dear Mrs. Ward always constantly Yours

Henry James

215 Autographed photograph of James.

216 Oil portrait of James by the British artist L. C. Powles.

Possibly the last portrait of James painted from life at his home Lamb House in Rye, England. See frontispiece.

217 Pencil sketch of James in the witness box by Max Beerbohm.

See illustration.

218 Beerbohm, Max. *To Henry James.*

Autograph manuscript, September 6, 1908. 1 p. A note in Beerbohm's hand suggests that the odd-numbered lines of the poem are by "M B" (Beerbohm) and the even-numbered lines by "E G" (Edmund Gosse). Inscribed: "For Mrs. Seymour Trower." See illustration.

RICHARD HARDING DAVIS (1864–1916)

This "ace" war correspondent spent much time in London, and many of his tales have an English background, i.e., *The Lion and the Unicorn, Our English Cousins, The Red Cross Girl* (which includes the prophetic *Invasion of England*), and *In the Fog*. He depicts English life in artistic and upper-class levels as seen through an American's eyes at the turn of the century. His works made a definite contribution to Anglo-American understanding.

219 *The Adventures of My Freshman. Sketches in Pen and Pencil.* Bethlehem, Pennsylvania, [1883].

First edition of the author's first book. H. W. Rowley was coauthor. Some of the sketches first appeared in the *Lehigh Burr* (1882–83).

220 *Our English Cousins.* New York, 1894.

First edition. The English edition was published the same year.

221 *Soldiers of Fortune.* New York, 1897.

First edition. Published in London the same year. An ALS of May 22 (n.y.), Davis to [William] Heinemann, concerning foreign translations of his work, is tipped in. Tipped in also is an ALS of July 4 (n.y.), Charles Dana Gibson to Louis E. Shipman. Gibson illustrated the book.

222 *A Year from a Reporter's Note-Book.* New York, 1898.

First edition. Presentation copy: "To the wife of the man [Gouverneur Morris] who writes stories such as the man who wrote these stories, would like to write   Richard Harding Davis July 5th 1907." The London edition appeared the same year with the title *A Year from a Correspondent's Note-Book.*

223 *The Lion and the Unicorn.* New York, 1899.

First edition. The London edition was published the same year. Presentation copy: "To Mother from Dick with his best love always   Marion '99."

224　*In the Fog.* New York, 1901.

First edition. No English edition was published.

225　*Soldiers of Fortune.* New York, 1902.

Play-Goers' edition, illustrated with scenes from the Augustus Thomas dramatization. Presentation copy: "To Thomas W. Ross with the best wishes of Richard Harding Davis   'they don't make them any better than you'."

226　ALS, New York, n.d., Davis to his brother, Charles B. Davis.

Presumably unpublished. About his writing and personal matters.

227　ALS, Hartford, Conn., n.d., Davis to his mother.

Presumably unpublished. About personal matters.

228　ALS, London, May 19, 1906, Winston L. S. Churchill to Davis.

Presumably unpublished. At Davis's request Churchill sends photographs for use in *Real Soldiers of Fortune.*

229　ALS, London, April 20, 1907, Winston L. S. Churchill to Davis.

Presumably unpublished.

·　·　·　·　·

I certainly considered the passage in your book wh[ich] is referred to in the cutting you sent me defamatory & injurious. It is altogether inaccurate, & quite possibly, though I have not taken legal opinion, libellous. But I did not attribute to you any malicious motive in writing it & publishing it. . . . I am glad to learn from your letter that my view of your motives was correct & that you did not desire to cause me any annoyance. The matter has not attracted much attention and may well be allowed to drop.

FRANCES HODGSON BURNETT (1849–1924)

Born in England, Frances Hodgson came to America in 1865 and settled near Knoxville, Tennessee. She married Dr. Swan Moses Burnett in 1873. Her most famous book, *Little Lord Fauntleroy*, an enduring Anglo-American juvenile classic, was dramatized with considerable success.

230   *Little Lord Fauntleroy*. New-York, 1886.

First edition with the imprint of the De Vinne Press on page 210. Later printings were done by J. J. Little & Co. The illustrations depicting the young hero in long curls and a velvet suit with a lace collar brought agonizing distress to generations of American schoolboys.

FRANCIS MARION CRAWFORD (1854–1909)

231 *A Tale of a Lonely Parish.* London, 1886.

First edition.

232 *Adam Johnstone's Son.* London, 1896.

First published edition, preceded only by the copyright issue with the title page dated 1895.

233 *Via Crucis A Romance of the Second Crusade.* New York, 1899.

First edition. Presentation copy: "James C. Young Esqr [']We have heard of amateur artists, amateur soldiers, amateur statesmen; but no one has ever heard of an amateur gentleman.['] p. 53, F. Marion Crawford."

234 *The Undesirable Governess.* New York, 1910.

First edition. The London edition was published a few days later.

235 *Uncanny Tales.* London, 1911.

First edition.

236 *The Doll's Ghost.*

Autograph manuscript. 8 pp. The story was published in *Uncanny Tales.* The scene is London.

AMY LOWELL (1874–1925)

A Boston Brahmin, Amy Lowell met Ezra Pound in England in 1913 and under his influence became the chief mentor of the "imagist" school of poetry.

237   *Dream Drops or Stories from Fairy Land by a Dreamer.* Boston, [1887].

First edition. Two copies are shown, in cloth and in wrappers. This is Miss Lowell's first book, a precocious work written at the age of thirteen.

238   *John Keats.* Boston, 1925.

First edition.

HAROLD FREDERIC (1856–1898)

239 *In the Valley*. New York, 1890.

First edition. The three-volume London edition appeared in 1891.

240 *The Damnation of Theron Ware*. Chicago, 1896.

First edition. Presentation copy to a close friend and correspondent of Frederic's: "To Earl Russell, with the compliments and good wishes of Harold Frederic May 6, 1896." *Damnation* is generally considered Frederic's most important and lasting work.

241 *Illumination*. London, 1897.

Ninth edition. English title of *The Damnation of Theron Ware*.

242 *March Hares*. New York, 1896.

Originally issued earlier in the same year under the pseudonym "George Forth." This is the first reissue with the author's name.

243 *Gloria Mundi*. London, 1898.

First English edition. Also shown is the first edition, published in Chicago in 1898.

244 *The Market-Place*. New York, [cop. 1899].

First edition.

245 ALS, London, February 27, 1886, Frederic to John Howe, a young friend on the staff of the Utica, New York, *Observer*.

Presumably unpublished. Frederic had been editor of this newspaper.

My dearest Boy:

When you get older you will discover that there are other and more important things in the politics of your great country—I never knew how great it was until I saw others—beside the question of Theo. Ballou vs. Tom Higgison. In the meantime, while we are both advancing in years, I wont bore you with further admonitions. If Gamaliel had been compelled to instruct his pupils from a distance of three thousand miles, I am afraid Saul of Tarsus would have been a sad ass, instead of a blooming saint. Only spell vermilion with one "l", and abscision, if you must use such a word, with one "s", and I will abdicate all my professional functions.

I am glad you liked Moffat. When I reflect upon it, I am ashamed ever to have doubted that you would like him. But I have been away so long, now, and fear so much to have lost my old standards, that I was not quite certain whether he would hit you off just right. But he is so enthusiastic about Utica and its people, and you, as well as my mother and others, speak so kindly of him, that I am constrained to believe he did justify in your eyes the great fondness I have for him. He asks to be most affectionately recalled to you all.

Atwell will be back in America a week or so after this letter reaches you. The postponement of the American Exhibition for a "year", threw him out of the place which I got created for him—he really had nothing to do but draw his salary—and, after a brief trip on the Continent, he is going back. He has, I believe, an offer from the *Graphic*. I try to hope that he has profited by the trip, and his experiences here, which have been as pleasant as I could make them: but I have to confess a grievous doubt about it now and then. If I don't find more improvement in you, when I next see you, than is apparent in him, I shall be tempted to commit assault and battery upon you. He has done nothing here but swell around here, and swagger, and instruct everybody, and generally make folks tired. I put up with it for a couple of months or so, and indeed to the end shall not discover my fatigue to him, but I have had enough!!!

I have been sending you Irish and other papers, and am glad you like them. Your pledge to send me papers in return was very welcome, but I have subjected it to considerable discount since. You ought not to say you will do things, my boy, unless you mean it; and you ought not to intend a thing, and then let it lapse through laziness. There is no comfort in that to your friends, and still less benefit to yourself. This by way of a gentle jog to your memory.

Among the papers I have sent to you—or was it to Mr. Bailey?—was an obituary article, upon the dear old Governor. It is no slouch of an achievment to get an obituary in the Thunderer, without a line of excision. Apropos of this, I wish you would say to John F. Seymour, when it is convenient and appropriate, that when the question of writing *the* biography of the Governor comes to be considered by the family, I beg not to be left out of account. It is a task which I have carried in my thoughts for a long time as one which could enlist all the power there was in me. They would find no other writer of equal rank who had the love for, or the knowledge of, the subject, which I possess. I expect now to be in America in June, and at the farthest I do not expect to remain in Europe more than one year after my return from the coming vacation. The place is pleasant enough, but I want to get back before I have lost touch with my own country. If next June the Seymours could go over the thing cursorily with me, and then let me have a year to saturate myself with the subject, I believe that on my permanent return, with the detailed materials before me, I could make the best biography America has ever produced. I make you my ambassador in this matter, and I pray you not to neglect or understate it.

Something in this preceding statement, perhaps, needs explanation. Men on salaries are not wont to speak so confidently of what they will and will not do. But I think I see independence close before me now. Tomorrow I shall write the last two chapters of my novel. There will be then a week of revision, of rewriting here and there; by March 10 the whole thing will be ready to send across the Atlantic to my publishers. I wish nothing to be said about it yet, for arrangements are half-made only, and premature publicity might damage me financially. But I have the backing of some of the best judges in England for saying that the thing will come perilously close to being the strongest story any American has written. I believe in it with an enthusiasm I never dreamed that my own work could awaken in me. Barrymore and I are at work—tentatively as yet—making a play out of the thing. Both together will make me independent but not a word about it yet.

If these beliefs of mine are not bubbles, I shall come back to America in 1887 with some money, with a reputation, and with the manuscript of a second story—the Mohawk Valley romance which I began five years ago—in such shape that two months' pointing up on the ground will make it in American literature what Henry Esmond is in English. Then I need never, please God, ask what time a paper goes to press again.

Healy spent Sunday at my house and I showed him the Irish part of your letter. He knows all about you, from the many times I have mentioned you in my discussions with him and O Connor and Parnell,—as an examplification of both the good and the meretricious points in the young Irish-American. He and I talked last night in the smoking-room of the House, about the idea of getting the eighty-five signatures of the Irish members on a single sheet of paper, to bring to your Branch when I come next spring. Would it be valued, do you think? And, if it would not make too much trouble, I think I should like to meet your Branch, when I come, and make them a little talk on the subject.

I speak of my vacation as settled. It is not. I have merely applied for it, and the answer will probably be here tomorrow. Even if it were granted, any big thing, like a heavy home-rule engagement here in May and June, or a War in the Balkans, would knock it all in the head. But if all goes smoothly I hope to be in Utica about 22.

> With love to all,
> Affectionately yours
> Harold Frederic

P.S. Will you kindly say to Will Philleo, Post office, that I am attending to his matter?

JAMES ABBOTT McNEILL WHISTLER (1834–1903)

Whistler's fame as an artist obscures his genuine ability as a writer. He attended West Point but failed in an examination. Later he declared: "If silicon had been a gas, I would have become a major-general."

246   *The Gentle Art of Making Enemies.* London, 1890.
First edition.

247   *Wilde v Whistler   Being an Acrimonious Correspondence on Art between Oscar Wilde and James A McNeill Whistler.* London, 1906.
One of a privately printed edition of 100 copies on large paper. The first edition was published in London in 1878.

248   Cary, Elisabeth Luther. *The Works of James McNeill Whistler. With a Tentative List of the Artist's Works.* New York, 1913.

249   Framed portrait of Whistler by William Nicholson.
With a short autograph note by Whistler. See illustration.

A portrait of Whistler (no. 249)

HENRY HARLAND (1861–1905)

After several novels of Jewish life written under the pen name of Sidney Luska, Harland moved to London about 1889. In 1894 he founded the *Yellow Book*, a quarterly that introduced many young writers in London to a public that otherwise might have ignored them. With Aubrey Beardsley as its first art editor, the magazine became famous as the expression of the nineties. Harland's masterpiece is probably *The Cardinal's Snuff-Box*. The scene is laid in Italy, and the subject is the romance of an English novelist and an English widow formerly married to an Italian nobleman.

250   *The Yellow Book   An Illustrated Quarterly*. Volume I (April, 1894).

251   *The Cardinal's Snuff-Box*. London, 1900.

First edition. Presentation copy: "To Percy and Mabel Dearmer with love from H. H. May 1900."

ROBERT (LEE) FROST (1874–1963)

252   *Twilight.* [Lawrence, Massachusetts, 1894].

First edition. This is the only existing copy of Frost's first book of poetry, which he had privately printed in an edition of two copies by a job printer in Lawrence, Massachusetts. One copy was later destroyed. Also shown is the facsimile edition (1966), with an introduction by Clifton Waller Barrett. See illustration.

253   *A Boy's Will.* London, 1913.

Proof copy containing autograph corrections.

254   *A Boy's Will.* London, 1913.

First edition, first issue. Presentation copy: "John and Margaret Outcasts of Lulu Flat from E. M. F. and R. F.   Castaways on an Island."

255   *North of Boston.* London, [cop. 1914].

First edition. First state of the binding. Presentation copy: "Leona from Rob and Elinor. Ledbury Eng July 1914." Leona was Elinor Frost's sister.

256   *My Butterfly.*

Autograph manuscript. 1 p.

257   *My November Guest.*

Autograph manuscript. 1 p.

258   *The Gift Outright.*

Typescript with autograph corrections and comment. 1 p. See illustration.

259   ALS, Beaconsfield, England, February 26, 1913, Frost to John F. Bartlett.

Published in *Selected Letters of Robert Frost,* edited by Lawrence Thompson (New York, 1964), pp. 65–66. About Frost's *Boy's Will,* which had just been published in

The only copy of Frost's first book of poetry (no. 252)

London. John Bartlett and his wife, Margaret, had been pupils of Frost at Pinkerton Academy, Derry, New Hampshire, and a lifelong friendship had developed.

Dear John:—

About now you are in receipt of my coverless book. Now you are reading it upside down in your excitement. What's the matter? You look pale. I see it all as true to life as in a melodrama. Your wife gathers around the table. The dog gets stepped on—the Indian Runner Dog. And Ruksh the dog utters a fearful cry. No canine cry is that, etc. It curdles the Annie Frazier River. A chair goes over.

"Wait," you say

"Wait a minute!"

"Hold on!"

"Give me time!"

"I tell you I can understand this if you give me time and don't hurry me!"

"In fact It isn't that I cant understand it,"

"I can understand it all right"

"But I can't believe it."

"It is what I may call the startlingness of the intelligence."

"Suppose I were to telegraph you from Raymond or some other center where things happen and news is manufactured that Sir Peg a Ramsey had demonstrated on the zylophone that there was more radium than neon and helium than yes than in no "

"You would be excited, wouldn't you?"

"Come own up. Of course you'd be."

"It would make all the difference in the world."

"You'd feature it—you'd call attention to it in a leader."

"Well it's like that—only—what shall I say?"

"Only more serious, more momentous."

"So unlike poetry—except Masefield's."

"If a man has anything he wants to break to us let him use prose—prose is his vehicle."

"Listen to this—it comes with too great a shock in verse."

"Get ready!"

"Eurt saw thguoht I lla fo erus erom ylnO"

"It is too, too much."

And so you run on till Mrs Margaret interposes with a woman's good sense!

"Perhaps if you read it right side up it wouldn't mean so much."

"It might not mean anything."

Still I think you will treat the book kindly for my sake. It comes pretty near being the story of five years of my life. In the first poem I went away from people*; in the one called A Tuft of Flowers I came back to them actually as well as verbally for I wrote that poem to get my job in Pinkerton as little

---

* and college.

Tommy Tucker sang for his supper, and Brer Merriam read it for me at a Men's League Banquet in Derry Village because I was too timid to read it myself.

Elinor will be writing to Margaret soon. She has been prevented from doing anything extra by various cares and anxieties of late. Lesley has resprained an ankle she sprained in Derry once and it makes a very bad case. She may be two months off her feet. The specialist in London was grave about it. That is hard on a mother. Lesley had a chance to see her own bones in the X-rays.

260   ALS, Beaconsfield, England, July 4, 1913, Frost to John Bartlett.

Published in *Letters*, ed. Thompson, pp. 79–81.

Dear John:—

Those initials you quote from T.P.'s belong to a fellow named Buckley and the explanation of Buckley is this that he has recently issued a book with David Nutt, but at his own expense, whereas in my case David Nutt assumed the risks. *And* those other people Buckley reviewed are his personal friends or friends of his friends or if not that simply examples of the kind of wrong horse most fools put their money on. You will be sorry to hear me say so but they are not even craftemen. Of course there are two ways of using that word the good and the bad one. To be on the safeside it is but to call such dubs mechanics. To be perfectly frank with you I am one of the most notable craftsmen of my time. That will transpire presently. I am possibly the only person going who works on any but a worn out theory* of versification. You see the great successes in recent poetry have been made on the assumption that the music of words was a matter of harmonised vowels and consonants. Both Swineburn and Tennyson aimed largely at effects in assonation. But they were on the wrong track or at anyrate on a short track. They went the length of it. Anyone else who goes that way must go after them. And that's where most are going. I alone of English writers have conciously set myself to make music out of what I may call the sound of sense. Now it is possible to have sense without the sound of sense (as in much prose that is supposed to pass muster but makes very dull reading) and the sound of sense without sense (as in Alice in Wonderland which makes anything but dull reading). The best place to get the abstract sound of sense is from voices behind a door that cuts off the words[.] Ask yourself how these sentences would sound without the words in which they are embodied:

You mean to tell me you can't read?
I said no such thing.
Well read then.
You're not my teacher.

He says it's too late
Oh, say!
Damn an Ingersoll watch anyway.

* Principle I had better say.

104

The Gift

~~WE GAVE OURSELVES~~ OUTRIGHT

The land was ours before we were the land's.
She was our land more than a hundred years
Before we were her people. She was ours
In Massachusetts, in Virginia,
But we were England's, still colonials,
Possessing what we still were unpossessed by,
Possessed by what we now no more possessed.
Something we were witholding made us weak
Until we found *out that* it was ourselves
We were witholding from our land of living,
And forthwith found salvation in surrender.
Such as we were we gave ourselves outright
(The deed of gift was many deeds of war)
To the land vaguely realizing westward,
But still unstoried, artless, unenhanced,
Such as she was, such as she might become.

R.F.

My history of the Revolutionary War which was the beginning of the end of colonialism.

R.F.

Frost's *The Gift Outright* (no. 258)

One-two-three-go!

No good! Come back–come back.

Harlam go down there and make those kids get out of the track.

Those sounds are summoned by the audible imagination[;] they must be positive, strong, and definitely and unmistakeably indicated by the context. The reader must be at no loss to give his voice the posture proper to the sentence. The simple declarative sentence used in making a plain statement is one sound. But Lord love ye it mustn't be worked to death. It's against the law of nature that whole poems should be written in it. If they are written they won't be read. The sound of sense, then. You get that. It is the abstract vitality of our speech. It is pure sound—pure form. One who concerns himself with it more than the subject is an artist. But remember we are still talking merely of the raw material of poetry[.] An ear and an appetite for these sounds of sense is the first qualification of a writer, be it of prose or verse. But if one is to be a poet he must learn to get cadences by skillfully breaking the sounds of sense with all their irregularity of accent across the regular beat of the metre. Verse in which there is nothing but the beat of the metre furnished by the accents of the pollysyllabic words we call doggerel. Verse is not that. Neither is it the sound of sense alone. It is a resultant from those two. There are only two or three metres that are worth anything. We depend for variety on the infinite play of accents in the sound of sense. The high possibility of emotional expression all lies in this mingling of sense-sound and word-accent. A curious thing. And all this has its bearing on your prose me boy. Never if you can help it write down a sentence in which the voice will not know how to posture *specially.*

That letterhead shows how far we have come since we left Pink. Editorial correspondent of the Montreal Star sounds to me. Gad, we get little mail from you. Affectionately

R.F.

Maybe you'll keep this discourse on the sound of sense till I can say more on it.

261 ALS, Ledbury, England, July 27, 1914, Frost to Thomas B. Mosher, a Portland, Maine, publisher.

Published in *Letters*, ed. Thompson, p. 129. About *North of Boston*, which Frost was preparing for publication in London.

Dear Mosher

I have thought of you in connection with my new book several times since its appearance. It has done so well here that I should almost venture to send you a copy in spite of your well-known predelection for the manner of the nineties. There have been long and remarkably favorable reviews from all

Last photograph of Frost (no. 262)

quarters from some of which you may have gathered what I am about. The two and a half columns in The Nation put the case very well and so did the shorter article in The Times. Hueffer's three columns in The Outlook rather bungled the technical question but on the whole I could not quarrel with it. All these you are likely to have seen. I am sending one or two others you would probably miss. Please tell me if on consideration you have reason to think you would care for the book and I shall be only too happy to see that you have one from my hand. You were one of the first to see me coming—you are nearly the only one thus far in America—and I should like to know that I had not lost favor with you at the same time that I was gaining it with really a good many important people over here.

Sincerely yours
Robert Frost

262 Photograph of Frost by Joe Clark, Detroit photographer.

Last photograph of Frost before his death in January, 1963. See illustration. Tipped in is a note dated November 13, 1962, on Clark's letterhead:

This informal portrait of Robert Frost by Joe Clark, was caught as Mr. Frost chatted with his friend Charles Feinberg in the Feinberg living room.

WILLIAM DEAN HOWELLS (1837–1920)

263   *My Literary Passions.* New York, 1895.

First edition.

264   *Heroines of Fiction.* New York, 1901.

First edition. Presentation copy: "Henry James with the affectionate remembrances of many other Christmases. W. D. Howells. New York, Dec. 25, 1902."

265   *London Films.* New York, [cop. 1905].

First edition.

266   *Certain Delightful English Towns With Glimpses of the Pleasant Country Between.* New York, 1906.

First edition. Autograph inscription:
>   Once, when I *sat peacefully at dinner, a feeling of the long continuity of English things suddenly rose in a tidal wave, and swept me from my chair, and bore me far away from the soup that would be so cold before I could get back. W. D. Howells. Christmas, 1906
>   * The shadow of a tear.

267   *Seven English Cities.* New York, 1909.

First edition.

268   *The Seen and Unseen at Stratford-on-Avon   A Fantasy.* New York, 1914.

First edition. Presentation copy: "Robert Herrick from his fellow idealist W. D. Howells. York Harbor May 23, 1914."

STEPHEN CRANE (1871–1900)

269   *The Red Badge of Courage   An Episode of the American Civil War.* New York, 1895.

First edition, first state. Presentation copy: "To Mr Irving Bachellor [*sic*], with the esteem and regards of Stephen Crane. Oct 14, 1895." Irving Bacheller's bookplate is pasted in.

270   *The Red Badge of Courage   An Episode of the American Civil War.* London, 1896.

First English edition in cloth and wrappers.

271   *Maggie   A Child of the Streets.* London, 1896.

First English edition.

272   *The Open Boat and Other Stories.* London, 1898.

First English edition. Presentation copy: "Dear Mrs. Moreton Frewen: You, with the rest of the world, have herein a further proof of my basic incapacity. However there are some stories of Americans and some stories of America in the book which may remind you of something better but, in any case, allow me to present my esteem Stephen Crane February 7, 1899."

273   *Last Words.* London, 1902.

First edition. No American edition has been discovered despite persistent rumors.

274   *Two Letters from Stephen Crane to Joseph Conrad.* [London, 1926.]

First edition. One of an edition of 220 copies.

275   *The Red Badge of Courage.*

Autograph manuscript and printer's copy. 176 pp. Earlier drafts appear on the verso of numerous pages.

TELEGRAMS-CRANE, BREDE HILL.
STATION-RYE.

BREDE PLACE,
BREDE,
NORTHIAM,
SUSSEX.

March 2nd-'99

Dear Mr. Collis;-

I am quite sure that the best thing
to do with the "Blue Hotel" is to take it to the
Westminster Gazette and sell it for about fifteen
pounds.I have always been a bit of a fad with them
and when ever I have to sacrifice myself upon the
alter of copyright,I have found them good priests.
The Editor has changed since my daybut I think you
will find them willing. This is the only thing which
I can think of .

I am very much obliged to you for the attention you have given the story. If you ever get
down into this dark corner of the world I am al-
-ways free and at home on Thursdays.

Yours faithfully

Stephen Crane

A business letter from Stephen Crane to an agent (no. 277)

Autograph manuscript. 6 pp. First published in *Lippincott's Magazine* (April, 1900) and the next year in Crane's collected stories, *Great Battles of the World.*

277   TLS, Brede Place, March 2, 1899, Crane to [?] Collis.

Published in *Stephen Crane: Letters*, edited by Robert W. Stallman and Lillian Gilkes (New York, 1960), pp. 214–15. Collis had an agency in London called the Author's Syndicate. See illustration.

Dear Mr. Collis:—

I am quite sure that the best thing to do with the "Blue Hotel" is to take it to the Westminster Gazette and sell it for about fifteen pounds. I have always been a bit of a fad with them and when ever I have to sacrifice myself upon the alter of copyright, I have found them good priests. The Editor has changed since my day but I think you will find them willing. This is the only thing which I can think of.

I am very much obliged to you for the attention you have given the story. If you ever get down into this dark corner of the world I am always free and at home on Thursdays.

> Yours faithfully
> Stephen Crane

278   ALS, Brede Place, May 5, [1899], Crane to Mrs. Moreton Frewen.

Presumably unpublished. Mr. Frewen owned Brede Place, Crane's residence in Sussex, England.

Dear Mrs. Frewen: I am an honest man above all and—according to promise— I must confess to you that on Saturday morning at 11:15—after dismal sorrow and travail—there was born into an unsuspecting world a certain novel called "Active Service," full and complete in all its shame—79000 words—which same is now being sent forth to the world to undermine whatever reputation for excellence I may have achieved up to this time and may heaven forgive it for being so bad.

> Yours faithfully
> Stephen Crane

279   Photograph of Crane as a cadet in the military school (Claverack College and Hudson Institute) at Claverack, New York.

A portrait of Crane in 1894 (no. 280)

280   Oil portrait of Stephen Crane in 1894 by Corwin Knapp Linson.

See illustration.

281   Two photographs of Crane in Greece in 1897.

Crane went to Greece to report the Greco-Turkish War.

282   Photograph of Crane with his wife, Cora, in England in 1899.

283   *Stephen Crane at Rye.*

Original water color by George Van Werveke, showing Crane in bed during his last illness. Published in the New York *Times Book Review*, May 26, 1929.

LOUISE IMOGEN GUINEY (1861–1920)

Miss Guiney, a Bostonian, fulfilled a cherished ambition when she went to England in 1895 to study at the Bodleian Library at Oxford. She died at fifty-nine at Chipping Camden, Gloucestershire, and is buried near Oxford.

284   *Robert Louis Stevenson   A Study by A. B. [Alice Brown] with a Prelude & a Postlude by L. I. G.* Boston, 1895.

First edition, privately printed. Presentation copy to Clara Erskine Clement Woods: "C. E. C. W. from L. I. G. 1895."

285   *Nine Sonnets Written at Oxford.* [Cambridge, Mass.], 1895.

First edition, privately printed at the University Press. Decorated by Bertram Grosvenor Goodhue. Original wrappers.

286   *"England and Yesterday"   A Book of Short Poems.* London, 1898.

Presentation copy: "To Harriet Agnes Anderson, from her loving friend and housemate who made it. L. I. G. Oxford, Christmas, A.D. MCMIV." Also inscribed, on the half-title page: "'Tomorrow for the States! for me, England and Yesterday!' Robert Louis Stevenson."

287   *Some Poems of Lionel Johnson*   Newly Selected with an Introduction by Louise Imogen Guiney. London, 1912.

First edition. Tipped in is an ALS, Oxford, February 24, 1912, Guiney to Gertrude [Hall]; presumably unpublished.

Gertrude Dear:

Where are you, and why didn't you come in the other day, when you returned the books? I was up in my den, a-pegging on the Oxford book (not mine) which I want you to watch for, about Easter. I have been absent eleven days out of this short month with my friends in Kent, recently bereaved of their father; I went down twice. This little collection from Lionel Johnson, with a reprinted essay of mine, is for you. I do hope you haven't flown to Bath or elsewhither.

Always yours,
L. I. G.

(NEWTON) BOOTH TARKINGTON (1869–1946)

Tarkington, celebrated for his juvenile stories and Midwestern romances, laid the scene of an early work in England. *Monsieur Beaucaire* is a romantic tale whose background is the corrupt and artificial society of Bath, England, in the eighteenth century. It was dramatized with considerable success.

288　*Monsieur Beaucaire.* New York, [cop. 1900].

Presentation copy to Tarkington's sister, Haute Tarkington Jameson, to whom the book was dedicated. Haute Jameson took the manuscript of the book to New York and prevailed upon S. S. McClure to publish it. The presentation inscription appears in two forms:

　(1) a typescript, 29 lines, signed by Tarkington and pasted in;
　(2) a shorter version, 26 lines, on the back of the frontispiece in Tarkington's hand and signed by him.

Three letters from Mrs. Jameson to her friend Mrs. James H. Manning are laid in.

289　*Monsieur Beaucaire.*

Original water color by C. D. Williams of the illustration used for the frontispiece. See illustration.

Original water color of the frontispiece in *Monsieur Beaucaire* (no. 289)

HENRY (BROOKS) ADAMS (1838–1918)

In 1861 Charles Francis Adams was sent to England as American minister. He was accompanied by his son Henry as private secretary. Henry remained in England for seven years, an important and happy period in his education as related in *The Education of Henry Adams*. Little of England rubbed off on him. His stay had rather the effect of intensifying his Bostonianism.

290 *Mont Saint Michel and Chartres*. Washington, 1904.

Privately printed. First edition. Presentation copy: "To Henry James from Henry Adams 1 Jan. 1905."

291 *The Education of Henry Adams*. Washington, 1907.

Privately printed edition of 100 copies with corrections in the author's hand.

292 ALS, Washington, March 6, 1881, Adams to Sir John Clark.

Presumably unpublished. Adams stayed at Sir John Clark's estate at Tillypronie, Scotland, during August, 1880. See illustration.

My dear Sir John

Knowing that my wife was about to write to Lady Clark I postponed a letter to you, waiting until my turn should come. I had thought once or twice of sending you a book or a novel, but they never seemed quite worth an ocean voyage when I came to reflect on it. You have politics enough of your own without being entertained with ours. You won't much care to hear about our profits and margins. You will take no interest in Leadville or Arizona silver-mines. You don't know which are our friends and which our enemies in the new administration. You have not even a passing acquaintance with Washington society and could not appreciate our favorite antipathies. In short you are much to be pitied and had better come over at once, but I don't see how I can really improve you[r] mind so long as you refuse to come. At best I can only give you an idea of what you lose.

In brief, you have lost a very indifferent winter; bad weather, bad roads, bad dinners, and very indifferent talk. I never have had less enjoyment, but am

much to be pitied and had better come soon at once, but I don't see how I can really improve your minds so long as you refuse to come. At best I can only give you an idea of what you lose.

In brief, you have lost a very indifferent winter; bad weather, bad roads, bad dinners, and very indifferent talk. I never have had less enjoyment, but am rather surprised to find how much I have had, notwithstanding all draw-backs. The truth is, the thing amuses me. One should always meet in society those one hates so those one loves; indifference poisons even champagne. Alas I have no one to hate; few I loath; my night but with passions. To sit at dinner next people to whom one does not bow, is a decided amusement if rightly understood; it animates wit and stimulates hatred. I can't get this sort of things in Europe and that is why I like my own lands.

lives as I view about politics, I always get a very active sentiment of personal antipathy to politicians, and really fail to tell them so. This makes up in warming their radical wisdom to a surprising degree. The resentment which mean words of one feel, is noncurable. A friend of mine, in high administrative office, said to me the other day when I recommended tact as a means of dealing with legislators: "Tact is of no use! A Congressman is a hog! You must take a big club and hit him on the snout!" Now, curiously enough, I would not tell that story to a Congressman without giving offence. I know, because I have once or twice tried. They actually took cold and are not cordial afterwards.

Nevertheless I always try to say something as pleasant as that, but still I am not populair, and few politicians come to my hours unless I ask them to feed. They would go anywhere to feed.

Part of an amusing letter by Henry Adams (r.o. 292)

rather surprised to find how much I have had, notwithstanding all drawbacks. The truth is, the thing amuses me. One should always meet in society those one hates or those one loves; indifference poisons even champagne. Abroad I have no one to hate: here I loathe my neighbor with passion. To sit at dinner next [to] people to whom one does not bow, is a decided amusement if rightly understood: it animates wit and stimulates hatred. I can't get this sort of thing in Europe and that is why I like my own land.

Little as I care about politics, I always feel a very active sentiment of personal antipathy to politicians, and rarely fail to tell them so. This results in winning their cordial aversion to a surprising degree. The resentment which mean minds often feel, is remarkable. A friend of mine, in high administrative office, said to me the other day when I recommended tact as a means of dealing with legislators: "Tact is of no use! A Congressman is a hog. You must take a big club and hit him on the snout!" Now, curiously enough, I would not tell that story to a Congressman without giving offence. I know, because I have once or twice tried. They actually look cold and are not cordial afterwards.

Nevertheless I always try to say something as pleasant as that, but still I am not popular, and few politicians come to me house unless I ask them to feed. They would go anywhere to feed.

Luckily there is much in this world that has nothing to do with politics. We never see a book. We never go to a play, or an opera. We never hear a song or a piece of instrumental music. We are completely of the iron-age, and indeed of the flint-period, in our intellectual surroundings. Still we manage to exist not without enjoyment, and we have now a gorgeous plan of buying a principality in Mexico and going down there with a few friends to be flint-period men again and enjoy the pleasure of living. You know how tame civilised life is, and how very small a hole was really made by Shakespeare, Wordsworth and such people in the crust of pure animalism. I want to revert to the ancestral type, and in this country it is not the politician; it is the Mexican Indian who knows life.

Poor Browning! He never got beyond Waring! Had he come over here, we would have made a poet of him.

First, however, I must finish my history which is to solve every known problem, philosophical, political, sociological and metaphysical. The task is rather a slow one. I can't turn out more than a volume a month, and at that rate I shall never use up the material I got in Europe. Still I do my best, and I rather expect that about five years will see me fling as many volumes at the head of the American public. The American public will growl, for I have some unpleasant stories to tell of them. As you know, the American public growls a good deal at having its face slapped; even poor Harry James was a victim; so I shall retire to Mexico and buy a *weal* on the shore of the Pacific Ocean so that I can always see the sun set over the water. My great objection to the east coast is that the sun sets over the land.

If you really meditate a journey, you had better wait till then, for by that time the necessary rail-roads will be built and you won't have to be scalped by

Apache Indians. This will be an advantage in some respects. You may take an interest in your scalp. I do not take much in mine, but then I'm growing old.

As for your poor, dear, little, old, melodramatic, blood-curdling continent, with its droll Greeks and Turks and French, and Dutchmen, it isn't real anyway. It ought to be put under a glass case in the British Museum. How you can help laughing when you think what a thoroughly absurd affair it is, I never can understand. Why on earth don't people mind their own business and stop fighting? Law bless me, how we *air* going to clean you all out!

Ireland too! I own up on that. It is certainly a tough case, and I don't see anything for it but for the landlords to sell out and emigrate. They can buy ten times as good land for the same money, and get out of Ireland besides. I never was in it but once and never was happy till out of it. As for sympathising with the landlord class who could actually make money by emigration, and not only make money but get away from that dreary, old, bog-trotting, water-soaked and blood-drenched hole. — No! they deserve to be shot for stupidity if for nothing else. Let 'em get up and *git*! they haven't learned the first notion of political economy. Their very laborers know more.

Are there any new books? any new men? or women? how are our friends? It is an age since I have heard from anyone and the newspapers talk of nothing but Mr Gladstone and Vernon Harcourt. The latter would be an excellent Irish landlord. I would like to take a pop at him myself. I see George Howard got his seat back, but I hear nothing more about Gaskell. Harry James has not written to me. Nor I to him. Robert Cunliffe has not written, tho' I did write to him. Lady Clark, like an angel, *has* written, and please give her our best and dearest love for the letter and for all her other kindnesses.

It is pleasant to have such a sunny recollection of any place as we have of Tillypronie. You have added a charming illustration to that little book of life which is usually called memory. As for the dogs! Never mind! I am going to have some. Poor little Boojum *is* yellow and not well bred. Did you ever hear the conversation of the owner of a yellow dog when asked what sort of dog he liked best?

"Wall! a yaller dog!"

"What sort?"

"Wall! I guess I like a yaller cur better'n anythin'."

So do we!

Ever affecly
Henry Adams

Sir J. Clark.

(WILLIAM) CLYDE FITCH (1865–1909)

Most successful American plays have been produced in London. More than a hundred have been performed in England since the days of William Dunlap and John Howard Payne. Some American dramatists, among them Clyde Fitch, William Gillette, David Belasco, and Augustus Thomas, have used English settings.

293 *Beau Brummel A Play in Four Acts Written for Richard Mansfield.* New York, 1908.

First edition. Presentation copy: "To my Father Merry Xmas. Clyde. 1908." Among the characters are George IV and Sheridan, resuscitated by Fitch to appear in Brummell's death scene.

WILLIAM (MORLEY PUNSHON) McFEE (1881–1966)

McFee was a marine engineer and a novelist. He came from England to America and lived here until his death.

294   *Letters from an Ocean Tramp*. London, 1908.
First edition of the author's first book. Signed by the author.

295   *Casuals of the Sea   The Voyage of a Soul*. London, 1916.
First edition. Perhaps McFee's greatest novel.

296   *Casuals of the Sea*.
Autograph manuscript. 818 pp.

CHRISTOPHER (DARLINGTON) MORLEY
(1890–1957)

Born in Haverford, Pennsylvania, this poet, essayist, and novelist was educated in England. In 1924 he joined with William Rose Benét to found the *Saturday Review of Literature*.

297 *Eighth Sin.* Oxford, 1912.

First edition of the author's first book. In original printed wrappers. 250 copies printed. Presentation copy: "This ('excessively rare') book is for Alice K. Shields (her first book) from her father's friend Christopher Morley. The Chaffing Dish, May 8, 1919. It was printed in Oxford, in November 1912—either 250 or 400 copies were printed, I really don't remember which—" With the copy is a partial proof (6 leaves from the first gathering), containing, on blank pages, an autograph poem of Morley's entitled *The Tryst*, inscribed for Mr. and Mrs. James Shields. The novel is about Morley's undergraduate days at Oxford.

EUGENE (GLADSTONE) O'NEILL (1888–1953)

298 *Bound East for Cardiff.* In *The Provincetown Plays,* first series. New York, 1916.

First edition.

299 *The Emperor Jones.* Cincinnati, [cop. 1921].

Presentation copy: "To Viola Atkins—With all pleasant memories of her visit to Peaked Hill. Come again! Eugene O'Neill."

300 *The Emperor Jones.* London, [1925].

T(HOMAS) S(TEARNS) ELIOT (1888–1965)

Poet, playwright, and critic, Eliot became the most influential poet of his generation. He was born in St. Louis, Missouri, went to Harvard, and read philosophy at Merton College, Oxford. Eventually he renounced his American citizenship and became a British subject. Perhaps his finest work, *The Waste Land* has become one of the most celebrated poems of modern times. Three translations—the French, German, and Spanish—have achieved wide circulation. In 1968 it was discovered that Ezra Pound had contributed significantly to *The Waste Land* by editing and shortening the text.

301   *Prufrock and Other Observations*. London, 1917.

First edition of the author's first volume of verse.

302   *The Waste Land*. New York, 1922.

First edition. Number 119 of 1000 copies printed.

A(LFRED) EDWARD NEWTON (1863–1940)

The most influential American writer on book collecting and an outstanding Anglophile. Newton's most important work is *The Amenities of Book-Collecting*.

303   *The Amenities of Book-Collecting and Kindred Affections.* London, 1920.

304   *Dr. Johnson   A Play.* Boston, 1923.

Number 10 of an edition of 585 copies on handmade paper signed by the author. Autograph inscription: "I never supposed when I was writing this, that I was writing a real play, but I did think that I was writing an essay on Dr Johnson, and as Jeff says to Mutt, 'I still maintain it's clever.' A. Edward Newton. Jany 17, 1924."

ANNE DOUGLAS SEDGWICK (1873–1935)

Anne Douglas Sedgwick was taken by her parents to England when she was nine and thereafter, with the exception of two years with her grandmother, lived in England and France. The scenes of many of her novels were laid in England, and she became noted for her subtle analysis of the relations of her English, American, and French characters. Her most noted works were *Tante*, *Adrienne Toner*, and *The Little French Girl*.

305   *Adrienne Toner*. London, 1921.
First edition.

306   *Adrienne Toner   A Novel*. Boston, 1922.
First American edition.

307   *The Little French Girl*. London, 1924.
First edition.

(HARRY) SINCLAIR LEWIS (1885–1951)

Lewis visited England many times. The manners and characteristics of the British seem to have fascinated him. He depicted English types in his novels *Babbitt* and *Dodsworth*.

308 *Babbitt*. New York, [cop. 1922].

First edition, first state. Presentation copy: "To Frank Hegger from Hal—Sinclair Lewis. Fisher's Island." Hegger was the brother of Lewis's first wife, Grace.

309 *Dodsworth A Novel*. London, [1929].

First English edition. Contains Lewis's *On an American Industrialist in England*. In this novel Lewis gave a vivid description of the emotions and reactions of an American visiting the old homeland for the first time.

310 ALS, New Haven, January, 1904, Lewis to Miss Clara Carpenter, a high-school friend.

Presumably unpublished. Lewis was nineteen at the time.

. . . . .

Don't you really do any thing in your spare time except write letters? Why don't you make out a reading list of classic authors, such as Coleridge, Thackery [*sic*], etc.? I am now reading Eliot, Dickens, Thackery, Tennyson & Wordsworth by turns.

311 TLS, Bearsted, England, Monday, [1921?], Lewis to John Drinkwater, the English poet, playwright, and critic.

Presumably unpublished. Regrets Drinkwater's inability to have dinner with him. Since Lewis is leaving shortly for a continental trip, he may not see Drinkwater again soon but hopes to see him "in England or America again, before too long."

312   TLS, New York, January 29, 1927, Lewis to Arnold Bennett.

Presumably unpublished.

.   .   .   .   .

Do you mind my saying that it seems to me that next to "The Old Wives' Tale," "Lord Raingo" is the best book you have done? This letter is . . . inspired . . . entirely by the tremendous eagerness with which I have read the book.

313   ALS, London, May 5, [1928], Lewis to Arnold Bennett.

Presumably unpublished. Invites Bennett to his wedding to Dorothy Thompson at the Savoy Chapel and a lunch following the ceremony.

ERNEST HEMINGWAY (1899–1961)

Although Hemingway was more prominently associated with Italy, France, and Spain than with England, the British character had its appeal for him and he created such individual characters as Lady Brett Ashley and her fiancé, Mike Campbell, in *The Sun Also Rises*. The English guide portrayed in *Green Hills of Africa* stemmed from his observation of the British on safari in Africa.

314   *The Sun Also Rises*. New York, 1926.

First edition.

315   *Green Hills of Africa*. New York, 1935.

First edition. Presentation copy: "To Jane [Armstrong] who copied it and put it into the English language—with very many thanks from her friend and admirer Ernest Hemingway."

316   *Green Hills of Africa*.

Autograph manuscript. 507 pp. Hemingway wrote in the manuscript: "The good writers are Henry James, Stephen Crane and Mark Twain. . . . All modern American Literature comes from one book by Mark Twain called Huckleberry Finn."

317   ALS, Paris, February 1, 1926, Hemingway to Ernest Walsh.

Presumably unpublished. Ernest Walsh was coeditor with Ethel Moorehead of *This Quarter; An International Quarterly Review of the Arts*, Paris (1925).

•   •   •   •   •

Have had your grand letter and your small letter. Carry the first around to read. . . .

Dont worry about me and MacAlmon. I'm really very fond of MacAlmon and besides would never hit any one. Have never hit but 2 gents outside of boxing. . . . Then only because they wanted to hit me. I dont brawl.

Dont let's any of us die of disease. Altho . . . I think that any form of dying can be made pretty swell. One of the things that I really look forward to is dying—but want to be at least 85 when it happens.

If Eliot was the most influential poet of his generation, Pound was the most indefatigable in assisting and promoting the younger poets, sometimes to their discomfiture as in the case of Robert Frost. Pound was born in Hailey, Idaho, and finished his formal education at Hamilton College, Clinton, New York, and the University of Pennsylvania. In 1907 he left for Europe and later made his way to London. Here he quickly became a close friend of the leading British poets. What Iris Barry calls "The Ezra Pound Period" lasted from 1912 to 1919. During the last two years of this period he was London editor of the *Little Review* (Chicago). He is described as having "exuberant" red hair and "a pale catlike face with greenish cat eyes." Critics generally consider the *Cantos* his most significant work.

318   *A Draft of XXX Cantos*. Paris, 1930.

First edition. Number 21 of 200 copies issued on Canson-Mongolfier Soleilvelin M.R.V. paper. The first English edition was published in 1933.

319   *Eleven New Cantos XXXI—XLI*. New York, [cop. 1934].

First edition.

320   *A Draft of Cantos XXXI—XLI*. London, [1935].

First English edition.

321   *Cantos LII—LXXI*. London, [1940].

First edition.

KENNETH (LEWIS) ROBERTS (1885–1957)

A chronicle of the Revolution, *Arundel* relates the near capture of Quebec. *Oliver Wiswell* is concerned with the Tories during the Revolution.

322   *Arundel*. Garden City, 1930.

First edition. Presentation copy: "For H. Bertram Smith, Jr. with best wishes— Kenneth Roberts." The inscription is written on Roberts's bookplate.

323   *Oliver Wiswell*. New York, 1940.

Number 786 of a special two-volume edition of 1050 copies numbered and signed by the author.

THOMAS (CLAYTON) WOLFE (1900–1938)

In 1926 Wolfe took two rooms on a little square in Chelsea and began work on his first book, *Look Homeward, Angel*. In *You Can't Go Home Again* he describes his experiences in London, including a riotous evening with one Lloyd McHarg, a thinly disguised portrait of Sinclair Lewis.

324 *You Can't Go Home Again*. New York and London, [1940].

325 ALS, London, November 28, 1926, Wolfe to William Cocke, a childhood friend from Asheville, North Carolina. Presumably unpublished.

· · · · ·

> My head and heart are slowly coming out of the hypnotic trance the English weather of the last three weeks has put them under. I want for a short time gay food, gay lights, voices, sounds, and, although I've taken monastic orders, at least a *look* at a pretty leg, and a face which does not run horsily to false teeth. I like England, but three months at a stretch is enough for anyone (except Rhodes scholars), and I've had five, and worked like hell.

326 ALS, Montreux, July 22, 1930, Wolfe to Melville Cane, a lawyer, poet, and, at the time, director of Harcourt, Brace.

Presumably unpublished. Wolfe discusses life at Montreux, "one of the most beautiful spots in Europe," his writing, and business matters.

Index of Authors